CALIFORNIA EDITION

WORKBOOK

HARCOURT SCIENCE

Harcourt School Publishers

Orlando • Boston • Dallas • Chicago • San Diego

www.harcourtschool.com

Harcourt

Contents

Harcourt

Extension

Harcourt

Reading in Science

Reading is very important in your becoming an independent learner—in being able to find, understand, and apply the information you need in the classroom and in your life. In science reading you are expected to find information, learn the meanings of scientific words, and put together ideas and observations. You can be helped in this reading and understanding by using the following suggestions.

To help you locate topics in *Harcourt Science* and most other science texts, use the:

- table of contents,
- titles of units, chapters, and lessons,
- headings and subheadings,
- index.

Look for and read these parts of a lesson in *Harcourt Science* to locate main ideas and other key information:

- Vocabulary Preview
- Investigate activity
- Process Skill Tip
- Find Out
- ✓ questions
- Picture captions
- Inside Story
- Summary
- Review
- Links
- Features

To help you recognize and read for specific kinds of information:

1. Recognize the text structure by looking for signal words.
   - compare/contrast—*however, but, some, different, instead, on the other hand, like, unlike, both, neither*
   - sequence or how-to—*first, second, next, then, last, finally,* or the use of numbered steps
   - cause/effect—*since, because, as a result*

Harcourt

2. Preview the material to see at a glance which material you already know something about and which contains new or unfamiliar topics.

3. First, read the questions at the end of a lesson or chapter. Then, read the lesson or chapter to find the answers. Also use the **Find Out** statements to help you identify what you need to find out while reading.

4. Construct graphic organizers or use the graphic organizers provided in the workbook to help you remember key points as you read.

5. Read the Science **Process Skill Tip** in each investigation to help you understand the meaning of a process skill. Do the Process Skill Practice page in the workbook for more information.

6. Write a summary of the main ideas of a lesson. Put in your own words (paraphrase) what you read about. Then compare your summary to the lesson summary in the book.

7. Look for comparison words such as *like* and *similar to*. These words can help you to understand something new by comparing it to something you already know about.

8. Read the entire sentence and sometimes the sentences around highlighted vocabulary to tell you what these words mean.

9. Make an outline of what you read to record main points.

10. Ask questions as you read. Write facts in one column on a sheet of paper. Write your questions in the column next to the facts.

11. Reflect on what you read. Write notes not only about what you read, but also about what you think, and why.

12. Use the **Review** in the text and the **Concept Review** and **Vocabulary Review** in the workbook to help you prepare for the chapter test.

Chapter 1 • Graphic Organizer for Chapter Concepts

How Plants Grow

LESSON 1
WHAT DO PLANTS NEED?

plants

1.

2.

3.

4.

LESSON 2
WHAT DO SEEDS DO?

Needs of Seeds

1. _____

2. _____

Plants Grow From

1. _____

2. _____

Parts of a Seed

1. _____

2. _____

3. _____

How Seeds Are Spread

1. _____

2. _____

3. _____

LESSON 3
HOW DO PLANTS MAKE FOOD?

What Plants Need to Make Food

1. _____

2. _____

3. _____

4. _____

How Plants Use Food

1. _____

2. _____

Harcourt

Needs of Plants

Materials

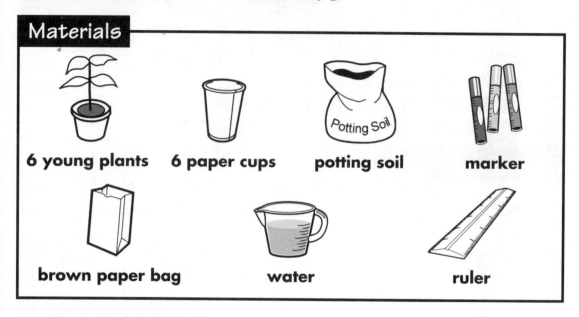

6 young plants   6 paper cups   potting soil   marker

brown paper bag   water   ruler

Activity Procedure

1 Put the plants in the paper cups and add soil. Make sure all six plants have the same amount of soil. Label two of the plants *No Water.* Put these plants in a sunny window.

2 Label two plants *No Light.* Place these plants on a table away from a window. Water the plants. Then cover them with a paper bag.

3 Label the last two plants *Water and Light.* Water these plants. Put them in a sunny window.

4 Every other day for two weeks, **observe** the plants. Check to make sure the plants labeled *No Light* and *Water and Light* have moist soil. Add enough water to keep the soil moist.

5 Record your observations on the chart on the next page. On the chart, **record** any changes you **observe** in the plants. Look for changes in the color and height of each plant.

Harcourt

Name _____

Plants	Day 1	Day 3	Day 5	Day 7	Day 9	Day 11
No Water						
No Light						
Water and Light						

Draw Conclusions

1. Which plants looked the healthiest after two weeks? _____

_____

Why do you think so? _____

_____

2. Which plants looked the least healthy after two weeks?

_____

_____

What was different for these plants? _____

_____

3. **Scientists at Work** Scientists often **compare** observations to reach their conclusions. Compare your observations of the plants to tell what things

plants need to grow. Make a list. _____

_____

_____

_____

Harcourt

Compare

When you compare, you identify how things are alike and how they are different. You can use your sense of sight when you compare. Comparing helps you gather information.

Think About Comparing

Suppose you plant two tomato plants in rich, dark soil in the back yard. You plant *Plant A* in a place where it gets full sun. You plant *Plant B* in a shady area. You give both plants the same amount of water. At the end of the growing season, *Plant A* is covered with juicy red tomatoes. *Plant B* has only a few tomatoes on it.

Plant A   **Plant B**

1. Compare the size of the two plants. _____

_____

2. Compare the leaf color of the two plants. _____

_____

_____

3. How are the plants different from each other? _____

_____

4. Which growing conditions were the same for both plants?

_____

5. Which growing condition was different? _____

_____

Harcourt

Use with page A5.

Name _____

Date _____

Concept Review

What Do Plants Need?

Lesson Concept

Plants have a variety of needs that must be met in order
for them to live and grow.

Vocabulary

| **roots** (A7) | **stem** (A7) | **leaves** (A7) |

Underline the best answer.

1. Plants get what they need from the sun, air, rain, and _____.

    A plant food   **B** soil   **C** rocks   **D** animals

2. The stem of a plant supports the plant _____.

    A above ground   **C** underground

    B before it sprouts   **D** after it dies

3. Leaves help plants use _____.

    A light and air   **B** fruit   **C** soil   **D** food

**Write the name of the circled part of the plant under each
picture. Use the vocabulary list.**

4.

_____

5.

_____

6.

_____

Name _____

Date _____

Sprouting Seeds

Materials

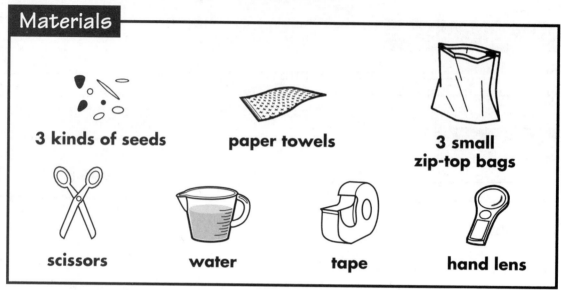

3 kinds of seeds　　**paper towels**　　**3 small zip-top bags**

scissors　　**water**　　**tape**　　**hand lens**

Activity Procedure

1 Start with a small amount of mixed seeds. Use size and shape to sort the seeds into three groups.

2 Cut two paper towels in half. Fold to fit into the plastic bags. Add water to make the towels damp. Do not use too much water or you will drown the seeds.

3 Put one group of seeds into each bag, and seal the bags. Label the bags *1*, *2*, and *3*. Tape the bags to the inside of a window.

4 Use a hand lens to **observe** the seeds every school day for 10 days. Use the chart below and on the next page to **record** your observations.

Seeds	Days				
	1	**2**	**3**	**4**	**5**
Group 1					
Group 2					
Group 3					

Name _____

 **Investigate Log**

Seeds	Days				
	6	**7**	**8**	**9**	**10**
Group 1					
Group 2					
Group 3					

Draw Conclusions

1. What changes did you **observe** in the seeds? _____

_____

2. How quickly did the changes take place in the different kinds of seeds?

_____

3. Scientists at Work Scientists **observe** their investigations closely to get new information. How did observing the seeds help you understand

more about seeds? _____

Investigate Further Repeat the investigation steps, but place the bag in a dark closet instead of in a window. **Predict** what will happen. **Compare** your prediction with the actual results.

My prediction: _____

_____

_____

My observations: _____

_____

_____

_____

Harcourt

Use with pages A10–A11. (page 2 of 2) **Workbook** WB7

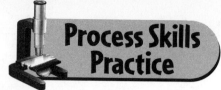

Process Skills Practice

Observe

You can observe directly with
your senses. Or you can use a
hand lens or microscope to
observe. Making an observation
is one of the most basic science skills.

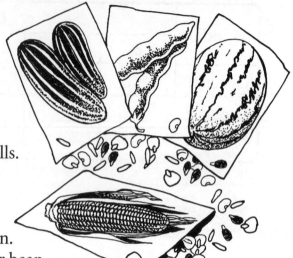

Think About Observing

You are planning a vegetable garden.
You order watermelon, corn, butter bean,
and cucumber seeds. When the seeds arrive,
they are all mixed together in one container! The company has sent colored
pictures of the seeds and the vegetables that will grow from the seeds. You
can use your observation skills to identify the seeds.

1. You spread the seeds out on a table. Which sense will you use to observe

the seeds? _____

2. In what ways are the seeds different from one another?

_____

_____

3. How could a hand lens help you with your observations?

_____

4. Describe what you will do to match the seeds to the seeds in the picture.

Step 1: _____

Step 2: _____

Step 3: _____

5. How did observing help you understand which seeds were which?

_____

_____

Harcourt

Name _____

Date _____

What Do Seeds Do?

Lesson Concept

Seeds produce seedlings that grow into new plants.

Vocabulary

seeds (A12)   **germinate** (A13)   **seedlings** (A13)

Fill in the blank with the correct vocabulary term from the list above.

Some plants form _____ to make new plants.

The small new plants are called _____. Some plants also can be grown from plant parts. Seeds grow to look like the adult plants they came from. All seeds have the same parts. Seeds need water

to _____. Seeds are spread to new places by air, water, and animals.

For each picture below, circle the plant part that makes seeds.

These sentences are mixed up. Number them in order.

_____ The sprout breaks through the soil.

_____ Leaves begin to grow.

_____ A root grows from the seed.

Name _____

Date _____

Food Factories

Materials

scissors	elodea	dowel or pencil	twist tie
empty 0.5-L plastic bottle	water	brown paper bag	watch or clock

 CAUTION Activity Procedure

1 **CAUTION** **Be careful when using scissors.** Use scissors to cut a piece of elodea (el•oh•DEE•uh) as long as the bottle.

2 Wrap the elodea around the dowel. Use a twist tie to attach it to the dowel.

3 Put the elodea into the bottle, and fill the bottle with water.

4 Put the bottle in a place away from any windows. Cover the bottle with the brown paper bag. After 10 minutes, remove the bag. **Record** any changes you **observe.**

My observations: _____

_____

5 This time, place the bottle in bright sunlight and don't cover it with the brown paper bag. After 10 minutes, **observe** the bottle. **Record** any changes you observe.

My observations: _____

_____

Name _____

Draw Conclusions

1. Did the elodea and water in the bottle look different after Steps 4 and 5?

_____ If they did, tell how they were different.

_____

2. What did you change between Steps 4 and 5? What remained the same?

_____

_____

3. Scientists at Work From what you **observed**, what can you **infer** about

the bubbles you saw? _____

_____

_____

Investigate Further Scientists often **measure** what happens in experiments. One way to **measure** what is happening in this experiment is to count the number of bubbles that appear. Put the bottle with the elodea in bright sunlight and count the number of bubbles that appear in one minute.

My observations: _____

_____

Then move the bottle out of the direct sun. Again count the number of bubbles that appear in one minute.

My observations: _____

_____

How are the two measurements different? **Infer** why they are different.

_____

_____

Harcourt

Name _____

Date _____

Infer

When you infer, you use what you have observed to form an opinion or give an explanation. That opinion is called an inference.

Think About Inferring

You and your friend are having a contest to see who can grow the tallest sunflower. You each plant a seed in your backyard. The seeds germinate and begin to grow. You both give your plants water and fertilizer. The two flowers grow taller every day. One day you go out to check your sunflower. You observe that the petals of your sunflower have holes in them. You use your hand lens to examine the whole plant from the flower to where the stem goes into the ground. You see a worm crawling on the flower.

1. What are you trying to explain? _____

_____

2. What are your observations? _____

_____

3. What information did you gather? _____

_____

4. What could you infer about the holes in the petal of the sunflower? How would you explain them? _____

_____

5. Think about your inference. Do you think your plant will grow or die? Explain your opinion. _____

_____

_____

_____

Harcourt

Use with page A19.

How Do Plants Make Food?

Lesson Concept

Plants make their own food through the process of photosynthesis.

Vocabulary

photosynthesis (A20) **chlorophyll** (A20)

For each pair of sentences, circle the letter of the correct statement.

1. **A** The substance in plants that makes them green is called photosynthesis.

   B The substance in plants that makes them green is called chlorophyll.

2. **A** Photosynthesis is the process plants use to make carbon dioxide.

   B Photosynthesis is the process plants use to make food.

3. **A** Plants use the food they make to grow bigger and make seeds.

   B Plants use the food they make to produce carbon dioxide.

Circle the parts of each plant where food that humans eat is stored.

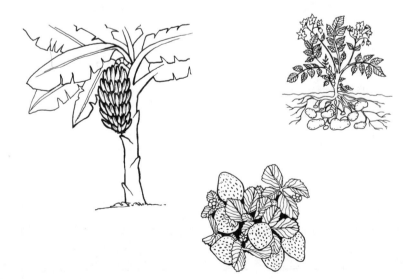

Harcourt

Recognize Vocabulary

root	seed	photosynthesis	stem
germinate	chlorophyll	leaves	seedling

Use the words above to fill in the blanks in the paragraph.

Two classmates decided to grow two plants for the science fair. First, they filled two clear plastic pots with good soil. They planted one

_____ in each pot. They placed one pot in a sunny window and the other in a closet. They observed their plants each day.

The seeds began to _____. One day the classmates

saw a _____ growing down into the dirt of each

pot. Next, a young plant called a _____ appeared.

Each plant was supported by a _____.

The classmates observed that the plant in the closet was no longer

doing well. Its _____ were not green. The

_____ in the plant needed sun to help the plant

make food. The process of _____ could not continue without light.

Draw the stages of the growth of plants. Label each picture. On the last picture, label as many plant parts as you can.

_____   _____   _____

Chapter 2 • Graphic Organizer for Chapter Concepts

Types of Animals

LESSON 1	LESSON 2	covered with	breathe with	how born	live where
Animal Needs 1. _____ 2. _____ 3. _____ 4. _____	Mammals	1. _____	2. _____	3. _____	4. _____
	Birds	5. _____	6. _____	7. _____	8. _____

LESSON 3	covered with	breathe with	how born	live where
Amphibians	1. _____	2. _____	3. _____	4. _____
Fish	5. _____	6. _____	7. _____	8. _____
Reptiles	9. _____	10. _____	11. _____	12. _____

LESSON 4

Extinction

Species can be

1. _____
2. _____
3. _____

Name _____

Date _____

Animal Homes

Materials

Animal Picture Cards

Activity Procedure

1 Select six Animal Picture Cards, or use the pictures on page A32. As you **observe** the cards, pay close attention to the types of homes the animals live in.

2 Describe each animal home you **observe. Record** your descriptions.

Animal Home 1: _____

_____

Animal Home 2: _____

_____

Animal Home 3: _____

_____

Animal Home 4: _____

_____

Animal Home 5: _____

_____

Animal Home 6: _____

_____

3 With a partner, discuss the different types of animal homes shown. Talk about the ways the animal homes are alike and the ways they are different. Then **classify** the animals by the types of homes they live in.

Harcourt

My Classification	
Description	**Animals in the Group**

Draw Conclusions

1. **Compare** two of the animal homes you observed. Tell how each home helps protect the animal that lives there. _____

_____

_____

2. What did you **observe** about the home of a Canada goose and the home of an albatross? _____

_____

3. **Scientists at Work** Scientists **classify** animals into groups based on what the animals have in common. How many groups did you classify the animals into? What were the groups? _____

_____

_____

_____

_____

Investigate Further Study the Animal Picture Cards again. This time, look at the body covering of each animal. Describe each covering. How can you use body coverings to **classify** animals? _____

_____

_____

Harcourt

Name _____

Date _____

Classify

Classifying is putting objects into groups according to how they are alike.

Think About Classifying

Your teacher gives you a worksheet showing different animals. You must
classify the animals. You decide to classify them based on how they move.
In the chart below, list the animals based on how they move.

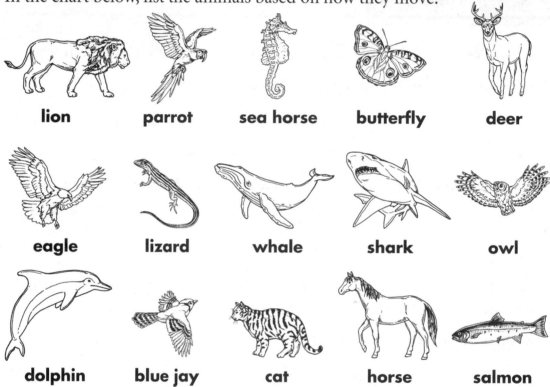

lion   parrot   sea horse   butterfly   deer

eagle   lizard   whale   shark   owl

dolphin   blue jay   cat   horse   salmon

Classifying Animals by How They Move		
Walking Animals	**Flying Animals**	**Swimming Animals**

Harcourt

What Is an Animal?

Lesson Concept

All animals have needs that must be met in order for them to live.

Vocabulary

traits (A38)   **inherit** (A38)

Fill in each blank with a vocabulary term.

All animals need food, water, air, and shelter. Different animals have different shapes and sizes. They have many different body parts. These shapes, sizes, and different body parts help animals get the things they need.

All animals _____ their features from their parents.

These features are called _____.

Underline the best answer.

1. The four things that all animals need are ____.
   A food, water, shelter, and air   **C** food, water, heat, and air
   B food, water, sunlight, and air   **D** soil, water, food, and sunlight

2. Animals that live on land get oxygen from ____.
   A the air   **B** food   **C** water   **D** sunlight

3. An animal's body produces energy from ____.
   A coal   **B** food   **C** air   **D** sunlight

4. The bodies of all animals contain ____.
   A water   **B** feathers   **C** fur   **D** scales

5. Caves, nests, turtle shells, and tunnels are all examples of ____.
   A animal shelters   **C** inherited traits
   B food containers   **D** water sources

Name _____

Date _____

Fur Helps Animals

Materials

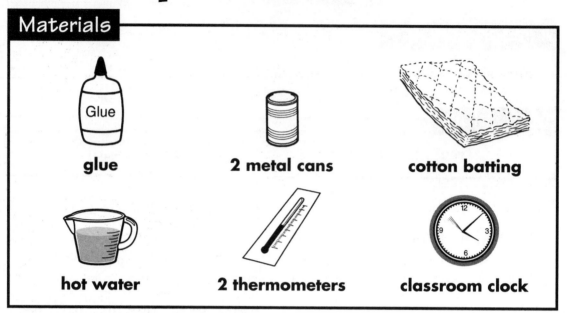

glue

2 metal cans

cotton batting

hot water

2 thermometers

classroom clock

Activity Procedure

1 Record your observations on the chart on the next page.

2 Spread glue around the outside of one can. Then put a thick layer of cotton around the can. Wait for the glue to dry. Then use your fingers to fluff the cotton.

3 **CAUTION** **Be careful with the hot water, it can burn you**. Your teacher will fill both cans with hot water.

4 Place a thermometer in each can, and **record** the temperature of the water.

5 **Predict** what will happen to the temperature. Check the temperature of the water in each can every 10 minutes for a period of 30 minutes. **Record** the temperatures on the chart.

Harcourt

Name _____

Time	Water Temperature in Can with Cotton	Water Temperature in Can Without Cotton
Start		
10 min		
20 min		
30 min		

Draw Conclusions

1. In which can did the water stay hot longer? Why? _____

_____

2. How did your prediction compare with the actual result?

_____

_____

_____

3. Scientists at Work Scientists often **use a model** to study things they can't observe easily. In this investigation, you made a model of an animal with fur. Why was using a model easier than observing an animal?

_____

_____

_____

_____

_____

Harcourt

Name _____

Date _____

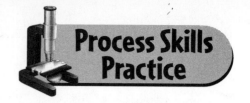

Use a Model

Using a model can help you study things you cannot observe easily.

Think About Using a Model

A polar bear has black skin. The polar bear's skin takes in the heat from the sun. You decide to make a model to test this idea. On a warm, sunny day, you take four ice cubes out of the freezer. You wrap two ice cubes in black plastic and two in white plastic. You put the two packets on a tray and set it outside in the sun. You want to find out which packet of ice cubes absorbs the heat more quickly. You time which packet of ice cubes melts faster. You feel each packet at five-minute intervals. You find out that the ice in the black plastic melted faster than the ice in the white plastic.

1. Why would you use a model to find out about the heat absorption of the

polar bear's skin? _____

_____

2. What observations can you make? _____

_____

_____

3. What comparisons can you make between the two packets?

_____

_____

4. Use your observations to infer why the ice in the black packet melted

faster than the ice in the white packet. _____

_____

_____

5. What might this model tell you about the polar bear's skin?

_____

_____

Harcourt

Use with page A41.

Name _____

Date _____

What Are Mammals and Birds?

Lesson Concept

Most mammals have fur or hair and give birth to live young. Most birds have feathers and lay eggs from which young are hatched.

Vocabulary

mammals (A42)   **birds** (A45)

Match each phrase with the best answer. Write the letter of the best answer on the line. Some may have more than one answer.

_____ **1.** These are traits mammals share.

_____ **2.** Birds are grouped based on the shape of these features.

_____ **3.** These cover most of a bird's body.

A feathers
B fur or hair
C lungs to breathe
D usually give birth to live young
E beaks
F feed their young with milk made in their bodies
G feet

Label each mammal with an *M*. Label each bird with a *B*.

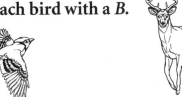

4. _____   **5.** _____   **6.** _____

7. _____   **8.** _____   **9.** _____

Harcourt

From Egg to Frog

Materials

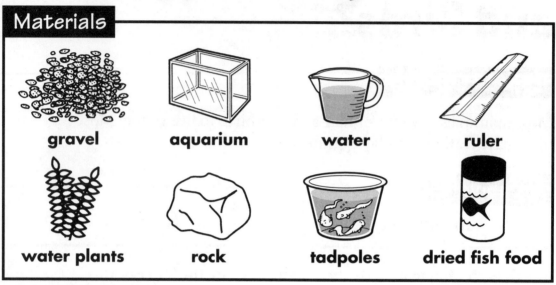

gravel   aquarium   water   ruler

water plants   rock   tadpoles   dried fish food

Activity Procedure

1 Put a layer of gravel on the bottom of the aquarium. Add 12 cm to 15 cm of water.

2 Float some water plants on top of the water, and stick others into the gravel. Add the rock. It should be big enough so that frogs can sit on it later and be out of the water.

3 Put two or three tadpoles, or young frogs, in the water. Put the aquarium where there is some light but no direct sunlight.

4 Feed the tadpoles a small amount of dried fish food once a day. Add fresh water to the aquarium once a week.

5 **Observe** the tadpoles every day. Once a week, make a drawing of what they look like. Use the charts below and on the next page for your data.

	Observations	Drawing
Day 1		
Day 2		
Day 3		
Day 4		
Day 5		

Harcourt

Name _____

	Observations	Drawing
Day 6		
Day 7		
Day 8		
Day 9		
Day 10		
Day 11		
Day 12		
Day 13		
Day 14		
Day 15		

Draw Conclusions

1. What changes did you see as the tadpoles grew? _____

_____

_____

2. When the tadpoles began to climb out of the water, what did their bodies

look like? _____

_____

3. Scientists at Work Scientists often repeat investigations to check the
accuracy of their results. Often the results will be different because of
uncertainty in the observations that were made. If you did the tadpole
investigation again, do you think the results would be the same? Explain
your answer. What could you do to collect better data?

_____

_____

_____

_____

Harcourt

Observe and Record

When you observe something, you use your senses of sight, hearing, smell, and touch. You can record your observations.

Think About Observing and Recording

Eva has a fish tank with tropical fish living in it. One day she notices that the glass sides of the tank have green matter on them. The filter is much too loud. An unpleasant smell is coming from the water. The side of the tank feels cold. She doesn't hear the hum of the heater that keeps the water warm.

1. Count how many times she used each of her senses in observing her fish tank. Record the numbers in the columns.

Sight	Hearing	Smell	Touch	Taste

2. Record what Eva saw.

She saw: _____

3. Record what Eva heard (or did not hear).

She heard: _____

She missed hearing: _____

4. Record what Eva smelled, touched, and tasted.

Smell: _____

Touch: _____

Taste: _____

5. Use all these observations to suggest what is wrong with the tank.

_____

_____

Use with page A49.

Harcourt

Name _____

Date _____

What Are Amphibians, Fish, and Reptiles?

Lesson Concept

Amphibians begin life in water, fish live all their lives in water, and reptiles are land animals.

Vocabulary

amphibians (A50)   **gills** (A51)   **fish** (A52)

scales (A52)   **reptiles** (A55)

Fill in each blank with a vocabulary term.

Animals that begin life in water, change in form, and then live on land are

called _____. _____ live in the

water, use _____ for breathing, and have body parts

that help them swim. _____ are land animals that are

covered with _____.

Label each animal as *amphibian,* *fish,* **or** *reptile.* **Circle the animals that have gills at some time during their lives. Cross out the animals that always breathe with lungs.**

 lizard   tadpole    salmon

1. _____   2. _____   3. _____

turtle   shark   toad

4. _____   5. _____   6. _____

Harcourt

Endangered Animals

Materials

reference books   graph paper   ruler

Activity Procedure

1 Find a list of endangered species from reference books or the Internet.

2 Choose five endangered animals from the lists. Look for information about how the numbers of these animals have changed over time. Find out how many of each animal are living now.

3 Make a bar graph for each animal you choose. Use one bar to show what number of animals were alive 10 years ago. Use a second bar to show how many are alive now.

4 Infer what will happen in the future to the animals on your graph. Explain your inferences, and share them with the class.

Name _____

Draw Conclusions

1. How did **using numbers** help you **organize your data** in this activity?

_____

_____

_____

2. What could happen that would change your **prediction**? **Record** your

ideas. _____

_____

_____

3. **Scientists at Work** Scientists **use numbers** to help them **organize their data**. They then use their data to make inferences. How did making a bar graph help you make your prediction about the future of the animals?

_____

_____

_____

Investigate Further Animals are not the only kinds of organisms that can become endangered. Find information on five kinds of plants that are endangered, and make a bar graph as you did for the animals.

_____

_____

Harcourt

Name _____

Date _____

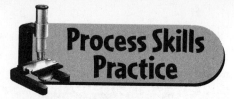

Process Skills Practice

Use Numbers and Infer

When you use numbers, you can summarize and try to understand data in a table. When you infer, you form an opinion about what the numbers show. The opinion is called an inference.

Think About Inferring and Using Numbers

The table below shows the populations of wolves and deer in an area between 1900 and 1940. The wolf and deer populations stayed about the same before 1960. Then sheep farmers began killing the wolves. Without predators, the deer population started to increase. Review the information in the table. Then use it to answer the questions below.

	Wolf Population	Deer Population
1900	850	10,000
1910	500	15,000
1920	400	22,000
1930	100	27,000
1940	10	36,000

1. Use numbers to explain what is happening to the deer population.

   _____

2. Use numbers to explain what is happening to the wolf population.

   _____

3. What can you infer about why deer are increasing while wolves are

   decreasing? _____

   _____

   _____

Harcourt

What Is Extinction?

Lesson Concept

Sometimes animal species become extinct. Extinction can be natural. People can also cause extinction. Laws protect some animals that are in danger of becoming extinct.

Vocabulary

extinct (A60)   **endangered** (A60)   **fossil** (A61)

species (A60)   **threatened** (A61)

Underline the best answer.

1. Evidence of an animal or plant that lived long ago is a(n) ____.
   A fossil   **B** species   **C** organism   **D** rock

2. A ____ is a type of organism.
   A species   **B** habitat   **C** population   **D** fossil

3. A species that no longer exists is ____.
   A endangered   **B** threatened   **C** extinct   **D** growing

4. Most species become extinct today because their ____ is destroyed.
   A predator   **B** habitat   **C** food   **D** mate

5. A species that is in danger of becoming extinct is ____.
   A threatened   **B** endangered   **C** healthy   **D** stable

6. There are ____ to protect threatened and endangered animals.
   A predators   **B** species   **C** hunters   **D** laws

7. A species that is on its way to becoming endangered or extinct is ____.
   A threatened   **B** dead   **C** increasing   **D** fossilized

Harcourt

Recognize Vocabulary

Match the definitions on the left with the terms on the right.

_____ 1. animal that lives in water its whole life

_____ 2. body parts that take in oxygen from the water

_____ 3. animal that has fur or hair

_____ 4. how animals get traits from their parents

_____ 5. animal that has feathers, wings, and two legs

_____ 6. land animal with dry skin, covered with scales

_____ 7. animal that begins life in water and moves on to land as an adult

_____ 8. species that are in danger of becoming extinct

_____ 9. a body feature an animal inherits

_____ 10. small, thin, flat plates that help protect fish

A amphibian
B bird
C fish
D gills
E inherit
F mammal
G reptile
H scales
I trait
J endangered

Write a riddle about these animals. Include the traits that each animal has in your riddle.

11. Mammals: _____

_____

12. Birds: _____

_____

13. Fish: _____

_____

14. Amphibians: _____

_____

Harcourt

Harcourt

Chapter 3 • Graphic Organizer for Chapter Concepts

Where Living Things Are Found

LESSON 1
WHAT ARE
ECOSYSTEMS?

1. The environment

_____
_____
_____

2. A population

_____
_____

3. A community

_____
_____

4. A habitat

_____
_____

LESSON 2
WHAT ARE FOREST
ECOSYSTEMS?

1. A deciduous forest

_____
_____

2. A tropical rain forest

_____
_____

3. A coastal forest

_____
_____

4. A coniferous forest

_____
_____

LESSON 3
WHAT IS A DESERT
ECOSYSTEM?

1. Hot deserts

_____
_____
_____

2. Cold deserts

_____
_____
_____

LESSON 4
WHAT ARE
WATER ECOSYSTEMS?

1. Freshwater
   ecosystems

_____
_____
_____
_____

2. Saltwater
   ecosystems

_____
_____
_____

Name _____

Date _____

Observing an Environment

Materials

wire clothes hanger

Activity Procedure

1 Bend your hanger to make a square. Go outside and place the hanger on the ground. Inside this square is the environment you will **observe**.

2 Make a list of all the things you **observe** below. Next to each thing on your list, **record** whether it is living or nonliving. Write *L* for living and *N* for nonliving.

3 Ask a classmate to share his or her list with you. **Compare** the environments each of you observed.

4 Choose a living thing you **observed** in your hanger environment. Talk with a classmate about which things in the environment help the living thing survive.

_____   _____

_____   _____

_____   _____

_____   _____

_____   _____

_____   _____

Harcourt

Name _____

Draw Conclusions

1. Describe the environment you **observed.** _____
_____
_____
_____
_____

2. How can you use **observation** to find out how an animal lives?
_____
_____
_____
_____

3. **Scientists at Work** Scientists learn by **observing** and by **gathering data.** They also learn from the data gathered by others. What did you learn about an environment from your classmate's data?
_____
_____
_____
_____

Investigate Further Observe a sample of soil in which an earthworm lives.

Describe the environment. _____
_____
_____
_____

Harcourt

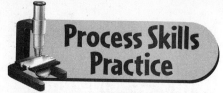

Observe and Gather Data

During experiments, you collect measurements like times and temperatures. At the end of the experiment, you arrange these measurements to make it easier to interpret the data.

Think About Observing and Gathering Data

Three third-grade classes in three different schools did a joint bug-observing project. Each class observed an environment once a week for four weeks. The classes gathered data and recorded their observations. Class 1 observed ants and an anthill on the playground next to the kindergarten sandbox. The students used a hand lens to observe the ants. Class 2 observed yellow banana slugs under a barrel in the woods next to their school. Class 3 found a caterpillar on a tree and observed it. Fill in the chart below with the classes' observations.

	Environment	**Nonliving Things**	**Living Things**
Class 1			
Class 2			
Class 3			

1. What do you think you can learn about a living thing by observing it?

_____

2. Why do you think Class 1 used a hand lens to observe the ants?

_____

_____

Harcourt

What Are Ecosystems?

Lesson Concept

The living and nonliving things that interact and affect each other form an ecosystem.

Vocabulary

environment (A80)   **ecosystem** (A81)   **population** (A81)

community (A81)   **habitat** (A81)

Underline the best answer.

1. A large number of frogs are observed in a pond. All the frogs in the ecosystem are ____.

   A a habitat   **B** an ecosystem   **C** a population

2. Other living things live in the pond. All the living things in the ecosystem are ____.

   A a habitat   **B** an environment   **C** a community

3. A ____ provides for the needs of the groups living in the pond.

   A population   **B** habitat   **C** ecosystem

4. Draw an ecosystem in the aquarium below. Make a habitat of water, rocks, and plants. Add a population of fish.

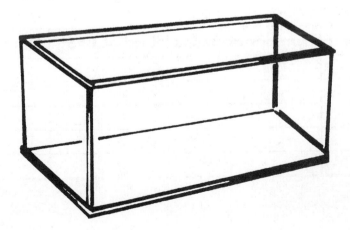

Harcourt

Use with page A83.

Variety in Forests

Materials

tray of beans,
labeled "Tray 1"

tray of beans,
labeled "Tray 2"

2 paper cups

Activity Procedure

1 Tray 1 stands for the trees in a tropical rain forest. Tray 2 stands for the trees in a deciduous forest. Each kind of bean stands for a different kind of tree.

2 Scoop a cupful of beans from each tray. Carefully pour each cup of beans into its own pile.

3 Work with a partner. One partner should work with the beans from Tray 1. The other partner should work with the beans from Tray 2.

4 Sort the beans into groups so that each group contains only one kind of bean.

5 **Record** a description of each type of bean in the data table below. Count the number of beans in each small pile. Record these numbers in the data table.

Tropical Rain Forest (Tray 1)		Deciduous Forest (Tray 2)	
Kind of Bean	**Number of Beans**	**Kind of Bean**	**Number of Beans**

Harcourt

Name _____

Draw Conclusions

1. How many kinds of "trees" were in each "forest"? _____

_____

_____

_____

2. Which forest had the most trees of one kind? Why do you think this

was so? _____

_____

_____

_____

3. **Scientists at Work** Scientists learn by **gathering, recording,** and
interpreting data. What did you learn from your data about variety

in forests? _____

_____

_____

_____

Investigate Further Suppose you want to find out what kinds of trees are
most common in your community. Explain how you could **use numbers** to

find out. _____

_____

_____

Harcourt

Name _____

Date _____

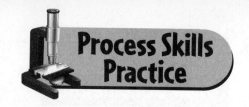

Use Numbers

Using numbers is one way to gather information and record data from an investigation. You can draw a conclusion based on the data you collect.

Think About Using Numbers

Roger lives on a farm. He writes to his pen pal, Teresa, "Our apple trees are doing well this year. We are taking lots of apples to the farmers' market every Tuesday." Teresa writes back, "I live in the city. I've never ever seen an apple tree. How many apples do you take to the market on one day?" Roger goes out into the barn. He sees apples in boxes, piled high. He doesn't want to count every one. He reads the side of one of the boxes and sees that there are 50 apples in each box. He writes that number in his notebook. He counts the boxes. There are 10. Roger writes to Teresa, "We are taking 500 apples to the market this week!"

Apples: 50 in each box
Boxes: 10

1. Why do you think Roger didn't want to count each apple? _____

_____

2. What did Roger want to investigate? _____

_____

3. What data did Roger gather and record? _____

_____

4. What conclusion did Roger come to? _____

_____

5. How do you think Roger used numbers to come to this conclusion?

_____

_____

Harcourt

Use with page A85.

Name _____

Date _____

What Are Forest Ecosystems?

Lesson Concept

There are four main forest ecosystems. These forests provide habitats for plants and animals.

Vocabulary

forest (A86)   deciduous forest (A87)

tropical rain forest (A88)   coastal forest (A89)

coniferous forest (A90)

Fill in the blanks below with vocabulary terms from above.

A _____ is an area in which the main plants are trees. The kind of forest where the trees have large, flat leaves that drop in the fall is

called a _____. A _____ grows in places that are hot and wet all year. That kind of forest has trees that grow

very tall and have leaves that stay green all year. A _____ grows where there is a lot of rain and it does not get too warm or too cold.

The trees in a _____ form seeds in cones.

1. In which kind of forest would you find this tree?

   _____

2. List the three layers of a tropical rain forest.

   _____   _____   _____

3. How does the triangle shape of conifers protect them?

   _____

   _____

Use with page A91.

Name _____

Date _____

 **Investigate Log**

Make a Desert Ecosystem

Materials

shoe box

plastic wrap

sandy soil

2 or 3 desert plants

small rocks

Activity Procedure

1 **Make a model** of a desert ecosystem. Start by lining the shoe box with plastic wrap. Place sandy soil in the shoe box. Make sure the soil is deep enough for the plants.

2 Place the plants in the soil, and place the rocks around them. Lightly sprinkle the soil with water.

3 Place your desert ecosystem in a sunny location.

4 Every two or three days, use your finger to **observe** how dry the soil is. If the soil is *very* dry, add a small amount of water. If the soil is damp, do not add water. Be careful not to water the plants too much.

5 Continue to **observe** and care for your desert ecosystem. **Record** what you observe.

My Observations: _____

_____

_____

_____

Name _____

Draw Conclusions

1. What kind of environment does your desert ecosystem model?

   _____

   _____

2. How does **making a model** help you learn about a desert?

   _____

   _____

3. **Scientists at Work** Scientists often learn by **making models**. What other

   types of ecosystems can you make models of? _____

   _____

Investigate Further How would getting rain every day change a desert
ecosystem? **Plan an experiment** in which you could **use a model** to find out.

   _____

   _____

   _____

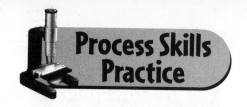

Make a Model

Sometimes you may want to observe something that is very large. You can make a small model and observe the model instead.

Think About Making a Model

You live in a climate that is hot and dry in the summer and cold and rainy in the winter. Suppose you make a model of a desert ecosystem in the backyard of your home. You make it during the hottest part of the summer. You plant some desert plants in sandy soil. Each day the blazing sun shines on your ecosystem. You give the plants a few drops of water once a week. The plants grow well. Then, when the summer is over, your ecosystem begins to change.

1. What is the purpose of a model? _____

_____

_____

2. What does this model teach you? _____

_____

3. What do you think will happen to your model at the end of the summer?

_____

_____

_____

_____

4. Draw a picture of the backyard desert ecosystem.

Harcourt

Name _____

Date _____

What Is a Desert Ecosystem?

Lesson Concept

A desert is an ecosystem found in areas that get very little rainfall.

Vocabulary

desert (A94)

Underline the best answer.

1. Hot deserts can have temperatures of over ____ during the day.

   A 23°C (about 73° F)   **B** 43°C (about 110° F)

2. The Taklimakan desert in China has ____ in the winter.

   A freezing temperatures   **B** notably high
   and blizzards   temperatures

3. The barrel cactus has parts that allow it to live in hot deserts. The barrel cactus does NOT have ____.

   A a thick skin   **B** very deep   **C** a thick stem   **D** very shallow
                             roots   roots

4. Desert animals get most of their water from eating plants or ____.

   A fruits   **B** vegetables   **C** other animals **D** nuts

5. You want to observe rabbits in the desert. Should you look for them

   during the day or during the night? Explain. _____

   _____

   _____

Harcourt

Name _____

Date _____

Make a Freshwater Ecosystem

Materials

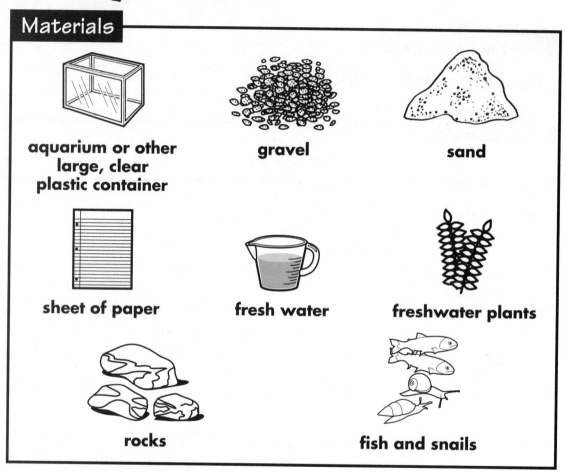

aquarium or other large, clear plastic container

gravel

sand

sheet of paper

fresh water

freshwater plants

rocks

fish and snails

Activity Procedure

1 Put a layer of gravel at the bottom of the tank. Add a layer of sand on top of the gravel.

2 Set the aquarium in a place where it isn't too sunny. Place a sheet of paper over the sand. Slowly add the water to the tank. Make sure you pour the water onto the paper so the sand will stay in place.

3 Remove the paper, and put the plants and rocks into the tank. Let the tank sit for about one week. After one week, add the fish and snails.

4 **Observe** and care for your freshwater ecosystem.

Harcourt

Name _____

Draw Conclusions

1. What are some things you **observed** in your freshwater ecosystem?

_____
_____
_____
_____

2. Why do you think you waited to add the fish to the tank?

_____
_____
_____
_____
_____

3. **Scientists at Work** Scientists often **make a model** of an ecosystem so they can **observe** it in a laboratory. How did making a model help you observe a freshwater ecosystem? How is your model different from a real pond?

_____
_____
_____
_____

Investigate Further What other kinds of plants and animals might live in a freshwater ecosystem? To find out, visit a pet shop that sells fish. Make a list of the freshwater plants and animals you find there. _____

_____
_____
_____
_____

Harcourt

Make a Model

You can make a model to observe something that would be difficult to observe in the classroom. When you make a model, you have to be careful, or your model won't work.

Think About Making a Model

Jeff made a model of a freshwater ecosystem. He put a layer of gravel on the bottom of a large, clear plastic container. He added a layer of sand. He poured water into the tank. The sand would not stay in place. It clouded the water. He had to start again. He put paper over the sand and poured the water in. He set his plants and rocks on top of the paper. When he saw what he had done, he had to take the plants and rocks out again. He took the paper off. Then he put the plants and rocks into the tank. He added the fish and snails right away. The fish did not do well. He took them out and put them back in his other aquarium. He let the water sit for a week. He added the fish and snails. They did well.

1. What mistakes did Jeff make in his model of a freshwater ecosystem?

_____

_____

_____

2. Infer why the fish and snails did not do well when Jeff put them in the

tank without waiting a week. _____

_____

_____

3. Write the correct steps for making a model of a freshwater ecosystem.

_____

_____

_____

_____

_____

Harcourt

Name _____

Date _____

What Are Water Ecosystems?

Lesson Concept

Water ecosystems may have salt water or fresh water.

Vocabulary

salt water (A100)	**fresh water** (A100)

Underline the best answer.

1. You go on a field trip to the aquarium. It is near the ocean. You see a display of a kelp forest. It is 10 meters (about 30 ft) deep. Which ecosystem are you looking at?

A freshwater   **B** saltwater

2. A beach is right outside the aquarium. Shallow salt water collects in the middle of some big rocks on the beach. The sun warms the water. Many plants and animals live in the warm, shallow water. What is the correct name for this area?

A pond   **B** river   **C** tide pool   **D** kelp forest

3. At the aquarium, you see a movie about ecosystems. People are swimming. When the people finish swimming, you see how still the water is. You see turtles crawling at the edge of the water. What kind

of ecosystem is this? How do you know? _____

_____

_____

Harcourt

Name _____

Date _____

Recognize Vocabulary

In the space provided, write the letter of the term in Column B
that best fits the definition in Column A. Use each term only once.

Column A

_____ **1.** a forest that contains mostly evergreens

_____ **2.** an ecosystem found in areas that get very little rainfall

_____ **3.** water that has lots of salt in it

_____ **4.** an area in which the main plants are trees

_____ **5.** everything around a living thing

_____ **6.** provides a population with all its needs

_____ **7.** a forest mostly made up of trees that drop their leaves each fall

_____ **8.** water that has very little salt in it

_____ **9.** a forest that grows in places that are hot and wet all year

_____ **10.** living and nonliving things interacting in an environment

_____ **11.** a group of the same kind of living things that live in the same place at the same time

_____ **12.** a forest that grows where it does not get too warm or too cold and where there is a lot of rain

_____ **13.** all the populations that live in an ecosystem

Column B

A fresh water

B coniferous forest

C desert

D environment

E ecosystem

F tropical rain forest

G coastal forest

H salt water

I forest

J population

K community

L deciduous forest

M habitat

Use with pages A78–A105.

Chapter 1 • Graphic Organizer for Chapter Concepts

Earth, the Water Planet

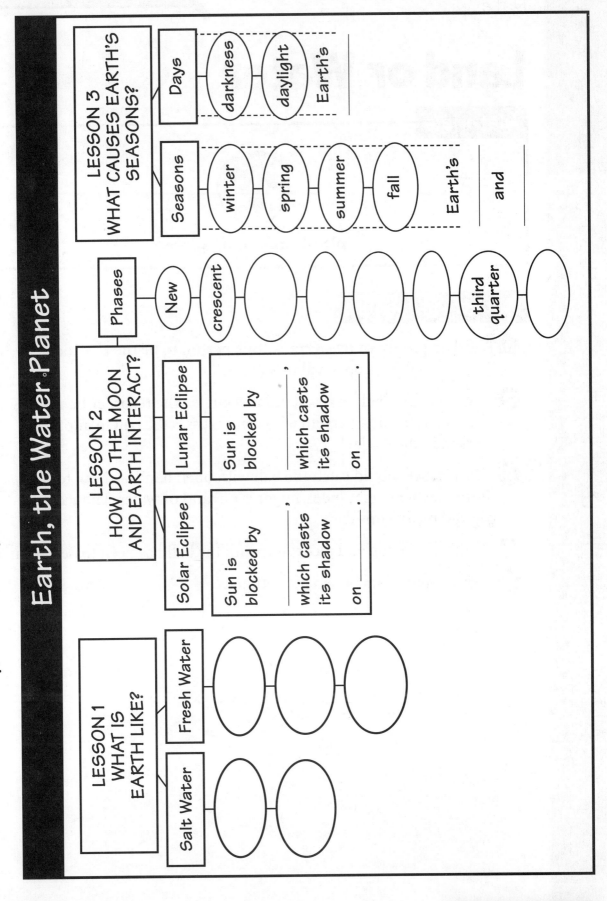

LESSON 3 WHAT CAUSES EARTH'S SEASONS?

Days — darkness — daylight — Earth's _____

Seasons — winter — spring — summer — fall — Earth's _____ and _____

Phases — New — crescent — ( ) — ( ) — ( ) — third quarter — ( )

LESSON 2 HOW DO THE MOON AND EARTH INTERACT?

Lunar Eclipse — Sun is blocked by _____, which casts its shadow on _____.

Solar Eclipse — Sun is blocked by _____, which casts its shadow on _____.

LESSON 1 WHAT IS EARTH LIKE?

Fresh Water — ( ) ( ) ( )

Salt Water — ( ) ( )

Land or Water

Materials

plastic inflatable globe

Activity Procedure

1 Work in groups of five. Choose one person to be the recorder. The other four people will toss the ball.

2 Have the four ball tossers stand in a circle. The recorder hands the ball to the first person, who gently tosses the ball to another person in the circle.

3 The catcher should catch the ball with open hands. Check to see if the catcher's right index finger is on land or water. The recorder should **record** this data.

4 Continue tossing and recording until the ball has been tossed 20 times.

5 Repeat Steps 3 and 4 two more times.

Harcourt

Draw Conclusions

1. Total your counts. How many times did the catcher's right index finger touch water? Touch land? _____

   _____

2. Where did the catcher's fingers land more often? Why do you think so?

   _____

   _____

3. **Scientists at Work** Scientists **use numbers** to **collect data**. Using your data, estimate how much of Earth's surface is covered by water.

   _____

   _____

Investigate Further You repeated this investigation 3 times. The more data you collect, the better your data becomes. How would doing the investigation 10 times change your data? Try it to find out.

_____

_____

Harcourt

Name _____

Date _____

Collect Data and Use Numbers

When you collect data, you make observations and record them. Using numbers helps you answer questions.

Think About Collecting Data and Using Numbers

You write to your cousin who lives in another state and tell her what a rainy year it's been. She writes back and asks what you mean by "a rainy year." You realize you need to collect data by finding out some rainfall measurements. You look up the rainfall numbers for one month in the summer and one month in the winter for this year and last year.

Rainfall in Summer and Winter	
August, this year	Week 1: 5 cm; Week 2: 7 cm; Week 3: 4 cm; Week 4: 2 cm
August, last year	Week 1: 3 cm; Week 2: 5 cm; Week 3: 2 cm; Week 4: 1 cm
February, this year	Week 1: 0 cm; Week 2: 2 cm; Week 3: 1 cm; Week 4: 3 cm
February, last year	Week 1: 0 cm; Week 2: 1 cm; Week 3: 0 cm; Week 4: 2 cm

1. How does collecting data by using numbers help you answer your

   cousin's question? _____

   _____

2. Why is it a good idea to collect rainfall totals for two months, instead

   of just one? _____

3. Total the rainfall counts. How much rain fell in August of each year? How much rain fell in February of each year? What is the total amount of rain for each year? Was this year really rainy compared to last year?

   _____

   August, this year: _____   February, this year: _____   Total: _____

   August, last year: _____   February, last year: _____   Total: _____

Harcourt

Use with page B5.

Name _____

Date _____

Where Is Water Found on Earth?

Lesson Concept

Earth is different from the other planets. It is the only planet with a surface covered mostly by water. Life on Earth would not be possible without water.

Underline the best answer.

1. Most of Earth's surface is covered by ____.

   A mountains   **B** glaciers   **C** water   **D** salt

2. Planets without water probably do not have ____.

   A soil   **B** life   **C** land   **D** craters

3. Water on Earth can be salt water or ____ water.

   A ice   **B** fresh   **C** sweet   **D** ocean

4. Fresh water is found in lakes, ponds, and ____.

   A large seas   **B** rivers   **C** oceans   **D** small seas

5. Most of the water on Earth's surface is ____ water.

   A salt   **B** frozen   **C** fresh   **D** river

The pie chart below shows that part of Earth's water is fresh water. The other part is salt water. Correctly label the parts of the chart "Fresh Water" and "Salt Water."

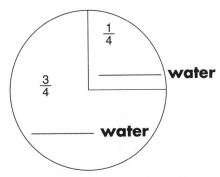

Harcourt

The Moon's Phases

Materials

lamp with no shade

softball

Activity Procedure

1 Work with a partner. Turn on the lamp. Your teacher will darken the room.

2 Have person 1 hold the ball and stand with his or her back to the lighted bulb. Hold the ball as shown on page B9. Continue holding the ball this way until the end of the procedure.

3 Have person 2 stand in position 1. **Observe** the ball. Make a drawing of the ball's lighted side.

4 Person 2 now moves to position 2. Turn toward the ball. Make a drawing of the lighted part of the ball.

5 Have person 2 move to position 3. Make a drawing of the lighted part of the ball.

6 Person 2 again moves, this time to position 4. Turn toward the ball. Make a drawing of the lighted part of the ball.

7 Switch roles and repeat the procedure so person 1 can observe the patterns of light on the ball.

Harcourt

Name _____

Draw Conclusions

1. What part of the ball was lighted at each position? _____

_____

_____

_____

2. The ball represents the moon. What does the light bulb represent? What represents a person viewing the moon from Earth? _____

_____

_____

3. **Scientists at Work** Scientists **use models** to make inferences to explain how things work. If the ball represents the moon, what can you infer that the different parts of the lighted ball represent? _____

_____

Harcourt

Name _____

Date _____

Observe and Infer

When you observe, you use your senses to gather information.

Think About Observing and Inferring

One night Isaac looked out his window and saw a big moon in the sky. He wanted to get some information about the moon by observing it. He went out every night to see how the moon had changed. He drew a picture each night for four weeks. Every night he saw a small change in how the moon looked. He made notes about what he observed. Here are some of the notes Isaac made.

OCT. 5
BIG, BIG MOON

OCT. 17
MOON LOOKS HALF GONE

OCT. 15
NOW ITS EVEN SMALLER, LESS THAN HALF

OCT. 18 A LITTLE, TINY, SLIVER

1. What observations did he make of the moon? _____

_____

_____

2. How could Isaac learn more about the moon through observations?

_____

_____

_____

_____

3. What inference could you make about why the moon looked different

over the time period of Isaac's observations? _____

_____

Harcourt

Use with page B9.

Name _____

Date _____

How Do the Moon and Earth Interact?

Lesson Concept

Phases are the different shapes the moon seems to have in the sky. The moon goes through its phases every $29\frac{1}{2}$ days.

Vocabulary

phase (B10)   **lunar eclipse** (B12)   **solar eclipse** (B14)

As you read the summary, fill in the blank with a vocabulary term.

The half of the moon that faces the sun is always lighted. As the moon moves around Earth, different parts of its lighted and dark sides face Earth. The moon's phase depends on the part of the lighted half that can be seen. The different shapes the moon seems to have in the sky are called

_____. There are solar and lunar eclipses. A _____

happens when the moon's shadow falls on Earth. A _____ happens when Earth's shadow falls on the moon.

Circle the term that best completes the sentence.

1. The half of the moon that faces the sun is always ____.

A dark   **B** lighted

2. ____ are the different shapes the moon seems to have.

A Phases   **B** Rotations

3. A lunar eclipse happens when Earth's ____ falls on the moon.

A shadow   **B** atmosphere

4. The moon's shadow falling on Earth is the cause of a ____ eclipse.

A solar   **B** lunar

Harcourt

Use with page B15.

How the Sun Strikes Earth

Materials

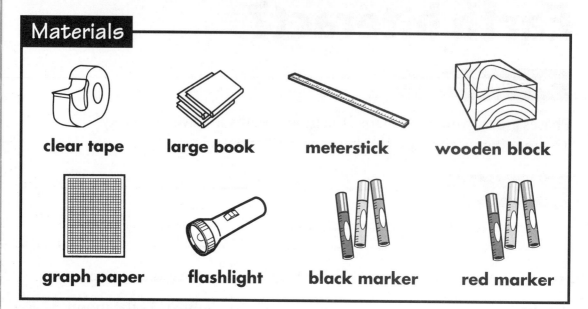

clear tape   large book   meterstick   wooden block

graph paper   flashlight   black marker   red marker

Activity Procedure

1 Tape the graph paper to the book.

2 Hold the flashlight about 50 cm above the book. Shine the light straight down. The beam will make a circle on the paper. If the circle is bigger than the paper, bring the light closer.

3 Have a partner use the black marker to draw around the light beam on the paper.

4 **Observe** the brightness of the light on the squares. **Record** your observations.

5 Keep the flashlight in the same position. Have a partner put the block under one end of the book and use the red marker to draw around the light on the paper.

6 **Observe** the brightness on the squares again. **Record** your observations.

Draw Conclusions

1. How many squares are inside the black line? How many squares are

inside the red line? _____

_____

_____

_____

_____

2. Inside which line was the light brighter? _____

_____

_____

3. Scientists at Work Scientists **compare** things to find out how they are
the same and how they are different. Compare the results of Steps 3
and 5 of the investigation. Do straight light rays or tilted light rays give
stronger light? Suppose the paper is Earth's surface. The light is the sun.

Which area would have warmer weather? Explain. _____

_____

_____

_____

Investigate Further Predict what will happen if the book is tilted even

more. Test your prediction. _____

_____

_____

Harcourt

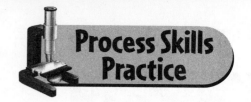

Compare

When you compare, you observe the properties of two or more things to see how they are alike and how they are different.

Think About Comparing

In September, Jean hung a picture of her favorite gymnast on the wall of her room. She hung it in a spot where the sun would shine on it at 3:00 P.M. each day, just when she sat down to do her homework. One day Jean noticed that the sun wasn't shining on her picture anymore. It was shining on her wall next to the picture. Jean thought this was interesting. She taped a circle of paper on the wall where the sun shone. She put the date and time on the paper. The next week, the sun was shining lower on the wall. She taped another circle of paper where the sun shone. Once a week she saw the sunny spot was lower on the wall and taped a circle of paper where the sun shone. She put the time and date on each circle of paper. By January 1, Jean had 16 circles of paper taped to her wall.

1. What did Jean observe about the sunny spot? _____

_____

2. What two things could Jean compare? _____

_____

_____

3. How else could Jean record her observations and comparisons?

_____

_____

_____

4. What could Jean infer from her observations? _____

_____

_____

What Causes Earth's Seasons?

Lesson Concept

Earth has seasons because its axis is tilted. This means the sun heats Earth's surface differently at different times of the year.

Vocabulary

rotation (B18) **axis** (B18) **revolution** (B18)

Underline the correct answer.

1. Earth rotates. Rotation is ——.

A a revolution

B the spinning of an object on its axis

C a season

2. Earth makes revolutions around the sun. Earth's revolution takes ——.

A one year

B a lunar year

C three months in summer

3. Earth's axis is tilted. If Earth's axis were not tilted there would be ——.

A only three seasons

B seasons every other year

C no seasons

4. Seasons in the northern and southern halves of Earth are ——.

A reversed

B the same

C moving

5. For part of the year, the North Pole points in the direction of the sun. This occurs during —— in the Northern Hemisphere.

A winter

B winter and summer

C summer

Harcourt

Use with pages B23.

Recognize Vocabulary

Vocabulary

phase (B10)	**lunar eclipse** (B12)	**solar eclipse** (B14)
rotation (B18)	**axis** (B18)	**revolution** (B18)

Match the definitions on the left with the terms on the right.

_____ **1.** an imaginary line that goes through the North Pole and South Pole

_____ **2.** it happens when the Earth's shadow falls on the moon

_____ **3.** the spinning of an object on its axis

_____ **4.** the movement of one object around another object

_____ **5.** it happens when the moon's shadow falls on the Earth

_____ **6.** the different shapes the moon seems to have in the sky

A lunar eclipse
B phases
C axis
D rotation
E revolution
F solar eclipse

Write the name of each phase of the moon described below on the line provided.

7. The moon looks like a round ball. _____

8. You cannot see the moon at all in the sky. _____

9. You can see a little less than three-fourths of the moon's

face. _____

10. You can see one lighted edge of the moon. _____

Harcourt

Harcourt

Chapter 2 • Graphic Organizer for Chapter Concepts

The Solar System and Beyond

LESSON 1
WHAT IS THE SOLAR SYSTEM?

Inner Planets

1. _____

2. _____

3. _____

4. _____

Outer Planets

5. _____

6. _____

7. _____

8. _____

9. _____

Other Objects in the Solar System

10. _____

11. _____

LESSON 2
WHAT IS BEYOND THE SOLAR SYSTEM?

Star Patterns

1. called _____

2. nightly _____

_____

3. seasonally _____

_____

Observing Stars

4. Using a _____

increases the number of stars that can be seen.

LESSON 3
HOW DO PEOPLE STUDY THE SOLAR SYSTEM?

_____

The Planets

Materials

pencil

paper

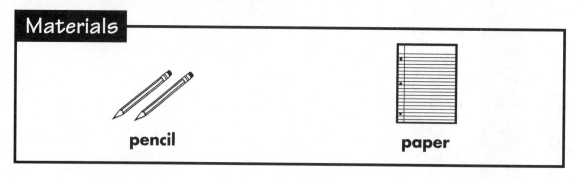

Planet Data			
Planet	Distance from Sun (in millions of kilometers)	Distance Across (in kilometers)	Length of Year (y = Earth year) (d = Earth day)
Earth	150	12,750	365 d
Jupiter	778	143,000	12 y
Mars	228	6,800	2 y
Mercury	58	4,900	88 d
Neptune	4,505	49,000	165 y
Pluto	5,890	2,300	248 y
Saturn	1,427	120,000	29 y
Uranus	2,869	51,000	84 y
Venus	108	12,000	225 d

Activity Procedure

1 Record your answers in the Ordering Planet Data Chart on the next page.

2 **Use numbers** from the data table to find each planet's distance from the sun. **Record** in your chart the names of the planets, beginning with the one closest to the sun.

3 **Use numbers** from the data table to find the distance across each planet. The planet with the shortest distance across is the smallest planet. Use numbers to **order** the planets by size. **Record** the names of the planets in order, beginning with the smallest planet.

Harcourt

Ordering Planet Data

Closest to the Sun to Farthest from the Sun	Smallest to Largest	Shortest Year to Longest Year

Draw Conclusions

1. Which planet is closest to the sun? Farthest away? _____

_____

2. Which is the largest planet? The smallest? _____

3. **Scientists at Work** Scientists sometimes **use numbers** to put things in **order**. Scientists have studied the same data you used in this investigation. How did using numbers help you realize the **space**

relationships between the planets? _____

_____

_____

_____

Harcourt

Name _____

Date _____

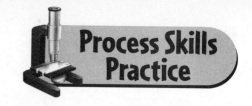

Use Numbers

You can use numbers to order things and put them into groups.

Think About Using Numbers

Suppose you want to group the planets in a number of different ways.
Look at the table that follows.

Planet	Distance Across (in kilometers)
Earth	12,750
Jupiter	143,000
Mars	6,800
Mercury	4,900
Neptune	49,000
Pluto	2,300
Saturn	120,000
Uranus	51,000
Venus	12,000

1. Study the distance across each planet. Group the four largest planets together. _____

_____

2. Now study the distances across again, and group the five smallest planets together. _____

_____

Harcourt

Name _____

Date _____

What Is the Solar System?

Lesson Concept

The solar system has nine planets that orbit the sun. Earth is one of those planets. Asteroids and comets are also parts of the solar system.

Vocabulary

solar system (B34)　　**orbit** (B34)　　**planet** (B34)

asteroids (B40)　　**comets** (B40)

As you read the summary, fill in the blanks with vocabulary terms.

An _____ is the path an object takes as it moves

around another object in space. A _____ is a large
body of rock or gas that orbits the sun. There are nine planets in the

_____. Earth is one of those planets. The sun is the
center of the solar system. It is a star made of hot, glowing gases. The

sun is closer to Earth than other stars are. _____

and _____ are also parts of the solar system.

Follow the directions for each question.

1. List three ways that Earth is different from the other inner planets.

_____

_____

2. List three ways the outer planets are alike. _____

_____

_____

_____

_____

Harcourt

Use with page B41.

Star Patterns

Materials

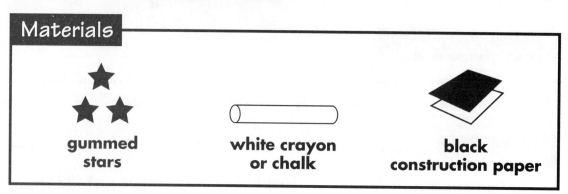

gummed
stars

white crayon
or chalk

black
construction paper

Activity Procedure

1 Take the stars in your hand. Hold your hand about a half meter above the paper. Drop the stars onto the black paper. Glue the stars where they fall on the paper.

2 **Observe** the stars. Look for a picture that the stars make. Use the white crayon to connect the stars to show the picture or pattern. You can connect all of the stars or just some of them.

3 Trade star patterns with other people in your class. See if they can tell what your star pattern is.

Harcourt

Name _____

Draw Conclusions

1. People have looked at the stars for thousands of years. Different people have seen different pictures in the stars. Why do you think this is so?

_____

_____

_____

_____

2. Some people look at a star pattern and see different things. A star pattern that looks like a water dipper to one person might look like part of a bear to another person. Look again at the stars on your paper. What

other patterns can you find in them? _____

_____

_____

3. Scientists at Work Scientists **compare** things to see how they are alike. In the investigation you compared your star pattern to objects you know about. What person, animal, or object does your star pattern look like?

_____

_____

Investigate Further **Observe** real star patterns. First choose a star pattern, and draw it as you see it with the unaided eye. Look at the star pattern again using binoculars or a telescope. Use another color to add anything to the pattern that you didn't see before. **Compare** what you saw in your two

observations. _____

_____

_____

_____

_____

Harcourt

Process Skills
Practice

Compare

When you compare things, you look for properties that are the
same and properties that are different.

Think About Comparing

Not everyone sees the same patterns of stars when looking at the
night sky. Each person finds a pattern that looks like something
familiar. Here you can see how the stars are actually arranged in
part of the summer sky. Below that, you can see the patterns
drawn in those stars by the ancient Greeks and Romans. Look
again at how the stars are arranged. Can you connect the stars to
make pictures of things or people familiar to you? Try it. Then
compare your drawings with those of your classmates. Did
anyone see the same patterns that you saw? How are they similar?
How are they different?

Use with page B43.

Harcourt

Concept Review

What Is Beyond the Solar System?

Lesson Concept

Groups of stars that form patterns are called constellations. More stars can be seen with a telescope than without one.

Vocabulary

star (B44)   **constellation** (B45)   **telescope** (B48)

Make a check mark in front of the statements that agree with your reading.

_____ **1.** A star is a hot ball of glowing gases.

_____ **2.** Stars are all the same distance from Earth.

_____ **3.** A group of stars that forms a pattern is a constellation.

_____ **4.** The reason stars seem to move is because Earth rotates.

_____ **5.** The stars rise above the horizon in the east.

_____ **6.** You see the same constellations at different times of the year.

_____ **7.** The North Star is far from Earth's axis.

_____ **8.** The constellations near the North Star circle around it.

_____ **9.** A telescope makes things that are far away look bigger and clearer.

_____ **10.** The astronomer Galileo used one of the first telescopes to see Saturn's rings.

_____ **11.** The first telescopes made things look thousands of times closer than they are.

Harcourt

Name _____

Date _____

Telescopes

Materials

1 thin (eyepiece) lens

1 thick (objective) lens

small piece of modeling clay

small-diameter cardboard tube

large-diameter cardboard tube

CAUTION | ## Activity Procedure

1 Press small pieces of clay to the outside of the thin lens. Then put the lens in one end of the small tube. Use enough clay to hold the lens in place, keeping the lens as straight as possible. Be careful not to smear the middle of the lens with clay.

2 Repeat Step 1 using the thick lens and large tube.

3 Slide the open end of the small tube into the larger tube. You have just made a telescope.

4 Hold your telescope up, and look through one lens. Then turn the telescope around, and look through the other lens. **CAUTION** **Never look directly at the sun.** Slide the small tube in and out of the large tube until what you see is in focus, or not blurry. How do objects appear through each lens? **Record** your **observations.**

My observations: _____

_____

_____

_____

Harcourt

Name _____

Draw Conclusions

1. What did you **observe** as you looked through each lens?

_____

_____

_____

2. Using your observations, **infer** which lens you should look through to **observe** the stars. Explain your answer. _____

_____

_____

_____

_____

3. **Scientists at Work** Some scientists use telescopes to **observe** objects in space. How would your telescope make observing objects in the night sky easier? _____

_____

_____

_____

Investigate Further Use your telescope to observe the moon at night. Record your observations. _____

_____

_____

_____

_____

Harcourt

Name _____

Date _____

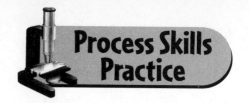

Observe

Telescopes can help you observe details of objects in the solar system.

Think About Observing

Look at the drawings of Jupiter. The larger one was based on a photograph taken through a telescope.

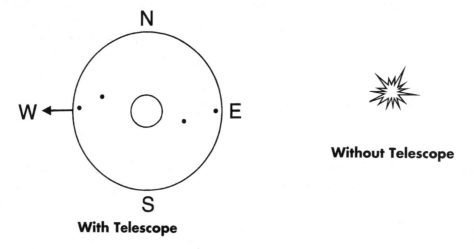

With Telescope

Without Telescope

1. What does Jupiter look like when viewed with the eyes alone?

_____

2. What does Jupiter look like when viewed through a telescope?

_____

_____

3. The small dots spreading out in a line near Jupiter are the planet's four largest moons. Italian scientist Galileo Galilei was the first person to observe these moons through a telescope. He watched them change position over the course of a few days and inferred that the moons revolved around Jupiter. What do you think Galileo observed that caused

him to make this inference? _____

_____

_____

Harcourt

How Do People Study the Solar System?

Lesson Concept

People use different kinds of telescopes, as well as crewed missions and space probes, to study the solar system.

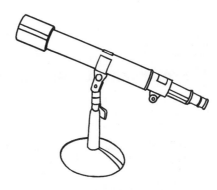

Answer the questions below about how people study the solar system.

1. How are these two telescopes different? _____

_____

_____

2. What kinds of problems occur with optical telescopes? List three ways scientists have worked around these problems. _____

_____

_____

_____

_____

_____

Harcourt

Name _____

Date _____

Recognize Vocabulary

Mark the vocabulary definitions *T* for true and *F* for false.
Rewrite the false definitions so they are true.

_____ **1.** A **planet** is a large body of rock or gas that orbits the moon.

_____

_____ **2.** A **telescope** is an instrument that makes things that are far away look clearer and bigger.

_____

_____ **3.** The **solar system** is the sun and the objects around it.

_____

_____ **4.** A **constellation** is a group of planets that forms a pattern in the sky.

_____

_____ **5.** An **asteroid** is a chunk of rock that orbits the sun.

_____

_____ **6.** A **star** is a hot ball of glowing rock.

_____

_____ **7.** An **orbit** is the path an object takes as it moves around another object in space.

_____

_____ **8.** A **comet** is a large ball of gas that orbits the sun.

_____

Harcourt

Use with Chapter 2.

Chapter 1 • Graphic Organizer for Chapter Concepts

Properties of Matter

LESSON 1
PHYSICAL PROPERTIES

Three Physical Properties of Matter:

1. _____

2. _____

3. _____

Three States of Matter:

4. _____

5. _____

6. _____

LESSON 2
SOLIDS, LIQUIDS, AND GASES

1. Matter is made of _____ .

Changing States of Matter

2. Adding heat changes a solid to a _____ .

3. Adding heat changes a liquid to a _____ .

4. Taking away heat from a gas changes it to a _____ .

5. Taking away heat from a liquid changes it to a _____ .

LESSON 3
MEASURING MATTER

1. The amount of space that matter takes up is its _____ .

2. The amount of matter in an object is its _____ .

Harcourt

Name _____

Date _____

Physical Properties

Materials

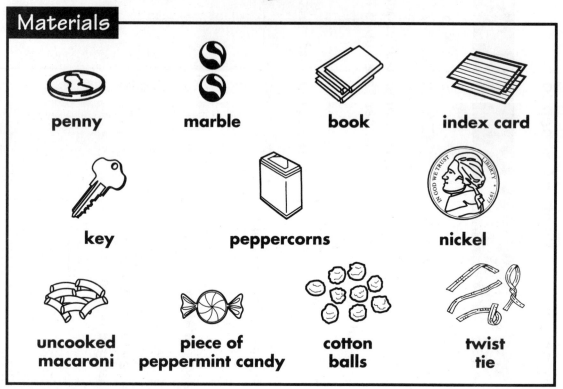

penny marble book index card

key peppercorns nickel

uncooked macaroni piece of peppermint candy cotton balls twist tie

Activity Procedure

1 Make charts like those on the next page.

2 Look at the objects you have been given. Notice whether they look shiny or dull. Notice how many colors each one has. **Record** your **observations**.

3 Touch the objects. Feel whether the objects are hard or soft. Feel whether they are rough or smooth. **Record** your **observations**.

4 Next, tap each object lightly with your fingernail. What kind of sound does it make? **Record** your **observations**.

5 Smell each object. **Record** your **observations**.

Harcourt

Name _____

	How It Looks			How It Feels			
Object	Shiny	Dull	Color	Hard	Soft	Rough	Smooth

	How It Smells			How It Sounds			
Object	Sweet	Sharp	No Smell	Loud	Soft	Makes a Ping	No Sound

Draw Conclusions

1. Which objects are hard and rough? _____

Which objects are hard and smooth? _____

Which objects are soft and rough? _____

Which objects are soft and smooth? _____

2. Compare your chart with the chart of another group. Are any objects in

different columns? Why? _____

_____

_____

3. Scientists at Work Scientists learn about the world by **observing** with
their five senses. Which of the five senses did you not use in the

investigation? _____

Investigate Further Make a list of the objects you have for lunch.
Use your sense of taste to **observe** these objects. Make a chart showing
what you observe.

Harcourt

Name _____

Date _____

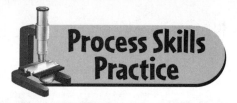

Observe and Record

You use your senses to observe the world around you. As you
make observations, you can record your data by writing it down.

Think About Observing and Recording

Dmitri asked his friend Rosa, a chef, to give a talk at his kitchen supply store.
Rosa spoke to Dmitri's customers about preparing a meal properly. Rosa
told the customers that when she shops, she looks carefully at everything she
buys to be sure it is fresh. She lightly squeezes a package of bread to be sure
it is not hard and stale. Even while she is preparing the food, she continues
to observe it. When she washes the lettuce for salad, she feels it to be sure it
is crisp. After the food is cooked, Rosa tastes it to see if she needs to add salt.
She also looks at the food on the plate to be sure it looks good.

1. What senses does Rosa use to observe the food? _____

_____

2. How do Rosa's observations help her prepare a meal?

_____

_____

3. Suppose you had these foods for lunch. For each food, circle the
observation to record what you would expect.

Food	Observation	
Peanut Butter	bitter	salty
Bread	fresh	stale
Celery	soft	crunchy
Cookies	sour	sweet

Harcourt

Concept Review

What Are Physical Properties of Matter?

Lesson Concept

Matter has many physical properties that you can observe by using your five senses.

Vocabulary

matter (C6) **solid** (C11) **gas** (C12)

liquid (C12) **physical property** (C6)

Answer the following questions about matter.

1. John and Tony go to the circus. They see a lion, a giraffe, and an elephant.

John, Tony, and the animals are matter because they _____.

A take up space **B** are breathing **C** are at the circus

2. John and Tony observe a tall clown on stilts and a tiny clown riding a tricycle. One clown has pink hair. Another clown wears a very large fake nose. What physical properties do John and Tony observe with their

sense of sight? _____

A smell and color **B** taste and feel **C** size and color

3. Tony smells something good. It's popcorn! Tony and John get bags of salty, buttery popcorn and cups of sweet pink lemonade. Taste and smell are physical properties of matter. Which words relate to these senses?

_____

A soft and fuzzy **B** light and dark **C** sweet and salty

4. John buys Tony helium balloons to take home from the circus. Which

state of matter is the helium inside the balloon? _____

A gas **B** solid **C** liquid

Harcourt

Use with page C13.

Name _____

Date _____

One Way Matter Can Change

Materials

 clear plastic cup

 2 ice cubes

 paper towel

 marker

Activity Procedure

1 Place the plastic cup on the paper towel. Put the ice cubes in the cup.

2 **Predict** what the ice cubes will look like after 45 minutes. Use your past observations of ice cubes to predict what will happen this time.

Record your prediction. _____

_____

3 **Observe** what's in the cup after 45 minutes. **Record** what you see.

_____

Was your prediction correct? _____

4 Mark the outside of the cup to show how high the water is. **Predict** what you will see inside the cup in the morning if you leave it out all night.

My prediction: _____

_____

5 **Observe** the cup the next morning. **Record** what you see. Compare your prediction to the actual result.

_____

_____

Harcourt

Draw Conclusions

1. What do you think caused the ice to change? _____

_____

_____

2. What do you think happened to the water when you left it out all night?

_____

_____

_____

3. **Scientists at Work** Scientists make **predictions** based on things they have **observed** before. What had you observed before that helped you

make your predictions? _____

_____

_____

Investigate Further Fill half an ice cube tray with water. Fill the other half with orange juice. **Predict** which will freeze first, the water or the orange juice. **Communicate** what you **observe**. _____

_____

_____

Harcourt

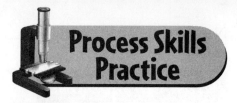

Observe and Predict

You use your senses to observe things that happen. A prediction is a statement about what you think will happen in the future. You can use your observations to help you make predictions.

Think About Observing and Predicting

Shannon did an experiment to let Brad observe how matter changes from one state to another. She put 2 cups of water into a pot and heated it on the stove. The water got hotter and hotter until it began to steam. The steam is a gas. Then Shannon carefully poured the water into a jar. Brad measured the height of the water in the jar. Steam rose out of the jar. Shannon put the jar in a warm closet for the night. In the morning Brad measured the water again.

1. When Brad observed the water in the pot, which of the three states of

matter was it in? _____

2. Brad observed the water while it was steaming. In which of the three

states of matter was the water? _____

3. Shannon heated 2 cups of water. Predict whether there were 2 cups of water or less than 2 cups of water when she poured it into the jar.

Explain your answer. _____

_____

4. Predict how much water was in the jar when Brad measured it the next

morning. Explain your answer. _____

_____

5. Draw two pictures of the water in two different states of matter. Label your drawings with the names of the states the water is in.

Harcourt

Name _____

Date _____

What Are Solids, Liquids, and Gases?

Lesson Concept

Atoms are small particles that make up matter. Whether matter is a solid, liquid, or gas depends on how tightly atoms fit together.

Vocabulary

atom (C16) **molecule** (C16) **evaporation** (C18) **melting** (C18)

Put a check mark in front of the statement in each pair that agrees with what you have learned.

_____ **1.** The atoms of solids do not move very much.

_____ The atoms of solids can slide past each other.

_____ **2.** Gas molecules stick together tightly.

_____ Gas molecules are not connected to each other and are not close to each other.

_____ **3.** Particles of liquid are more loosely attached than those in a solid. The particles can slide past each other.

_____ Particles of liquid are like those in a solid.

_____ **4.** The state of matter can be changed by adding or taking away heat.

_____ The state of matter can be changed by touching the particles.

_____ **5.** Gas particles are the basic building blocks of matter.

_____ Atoms are the basic building blocks of matter.

_____ **6.** Melting is the process by which a solid becomes a liquid.

_____ Evaporation is the process by which a solid becomes a liquid.

Measuring Mass and Volume

Materials

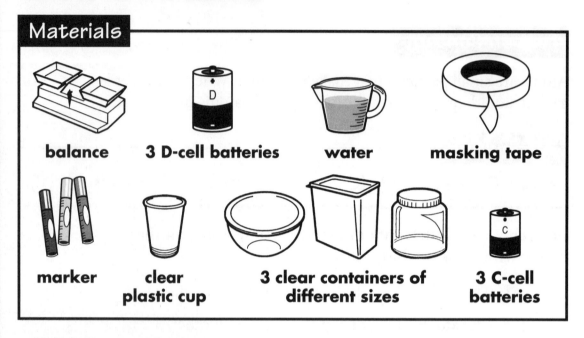

balance	**3 D-cell batteries**	**water**	**masking tape**
marker	**clear plastic cup**	**3 clear containers of different sizes**	**3 C-cell batteries**

Activity Procedure

Part A

1 Put a C-cell in the pan on the left side of the balance. Put a D-cell in the pan on the right side. **Record** which battery is heavier.

2 Add C-cells to the left side and D-cells to the right side until the pans are balanced. You may need to use some of the small masses from the balance to make the cells balance perfectly. **Record** the number of C-cells and D-cells you use.

Part B

3 Fill the cup half-full with water. Use a piece of tape to mark how high the water is in the cup. **Predict** how high the water will be in each container if you pour the water into it. Mark each prediction with a piece of tape. Write *P* (for *Predict*) on the tape.

4 Pour the water into the next container. Mark the height of the water with a piece of tape. Write *A* (for *Actual*) on the tape.

Harcourt

5 Repeat Step 4 for each of the other containers.

Draw Conclusions

1. **Compare** the numbers of C-cells and D-cells it took to balance the pans. **Draw a conclusion** from these numbers about the masses of the cells.

_____

_____

_____

2. Describe the height of the water in each container. Why did the same amount of water look different in the different containers?

_____

_____

_____

_____

_____

3. **Scientists at Work** Scientists **measure** matter by using tools that are marked with standard amounts. What was the standard amount you used

in this activity to measure the water? _____

_____

Name _____

Date _____

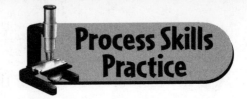
Measure

Measuring is a way to observe and compare things accurately. You can use an instrument like a ruler or a balance to measure the size of an object.

Think About Measuring

Tina brought two boxes of cookies to class. One box was larger than the other. She invited three classmates to look at the boxes and predict which had more mass. Two classmates chose the larger box. She put the two boxes on the balance. Look at the picture.

1. What does the balance show about the two boxes of cookies?

_____

_____

Tina also brought juice to share equally with her group. But none of the glasses she brought were the same size. Before she poured the juice, Tina wanted to be sure each classmate had the same amount. For each classmate, she used a measuring cup and measured 1 cup. Then she poured the juice into a glass. She noticed that the level of the juice was different in all the glasses.

12-oz. glass   **15-oz. glass**   **20-oz. glass**

2. Why was it a good idea that Tina measured the juice in a measuring cup

before pouring it into each glass? _____

_____

_____

Use with page C21.

Harcourt

How Can Matter Be Measured?

Lesson Concept

Volume is the amount of space an object takes up. Mass is how much matter is in an object. Different objects can have the same volume but different masses.

Vocabulary

volume (C22)   **mass** (C24)

Put a check mark in front of the statement in each pair that agrees with what you have learned.

_____ **1.** The amount of space matter takes up is called mass.

_____ The amount of space matter takes up is called volume.

_____ **2.** You can tell how much mass an object has just by looking at it.

_____ You can measure an object to tell how much mass it has.

_____ **3.** Mass is the amount of liquid in an object.

_____ Mass is the amount of matter in an object.

_____ **4.** Air is a gas that cannot be seen and has no mass.

_____ Air and other gases have mass.

_____ **5.** Different kinds of matter can take up the same amount of space but have different masses.

_____ If different kinds of matter take up the same amount of space, they have the same mass.

Harcourt

Recognize Vocabulary

Match each term in Column A with its definition in Column B.

Column A

_____ **1.** It does not have a definite shape or a definite volume.

_____ **2.** They are the basic building blocks of matter.

_____ **3.** This is the process in which a liquid becomes a gas.

_____ **4.** This is the amount of space matter takes up.

_____ **5.** It is anything you can observe about an object by using your senses.

_____ **6.** All matter has volume and ____.

_____ **7.** It is anything that takes up space.

_____ **8.** It takes up a specific amount of space and has a definite shape.

_____ **9.** It has a volume that stays the same, but it can change its shape.

_____ **10.** Atoms that are linked together.

_____ **11.** The process of change from a solid to a liquid.

Column B

A mass

B volume

C evaporation

D solid

E matter

F atoms

G physical property

H liquid

I gas

J molecules

K melting

Harcourt

Chapter 2 • Graphic Organizer for Chapter Concepts

Changes in Matter

LESSON 1
PHYSICAL CHANGES

Ways Matter Can Change Physically and Still Be the Same Matter

1. _____

2. _____

3. _____

Ways to Physically Mix Matter

1. _____

2. _____

LESSON 2
CHEMICAL CHANGES

During a chemical change, _____

Examples of Chemical Changes

1. _____

2. _____

How Chemical Changes Are Used

1. _____

2. _____

3. _____

Name _____

Date _____

Separate a Mixture

Materials

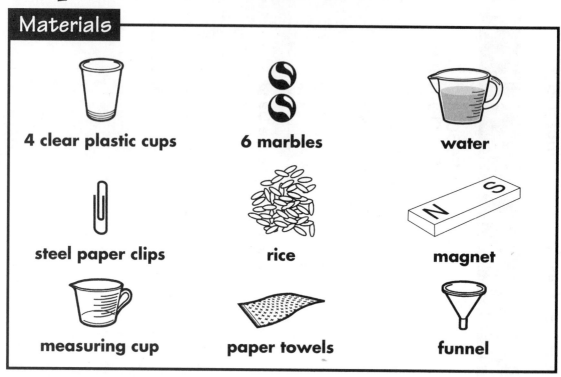

4 clear plastic cups

6 marbles

water

steel paper clips

rice

magnet

measuring cup

paper towels

funnel

Activity Procedure

1 In one cup, make a mixture of marbles and water. Plan a way to separate the marbles from the water. Try it. **Record** your method and your results.

My method: _____

My results: _____

2 In another cup, make a mixture of marbles, paper clips, and rice. Plan a way to separate the mixture. Try it. **Record** your method and your results.

My method: _____

My results: _____

Harcourt

3 If your method doesn't work, plan a different way to separate the mixture. Try different methods until you find one that works. Try using the magnet. **Record** your method and your results.

My method: _____

My results: _____

4 In another cup, mix $\frac{1}{4}$ cup of rice with 1 cup of water. How could you separate the rice from the water? **Record** your ideas.

My ideas: _____

5 Make a filter with the paper towels and the funnel. **Predict** how this tool could be used to separate the mixture. Then use the filter to separate the mixture.

My prediction: _____

Draw Conclusions

1. When would it be easy to use only your hands to separate a mixture?

_____

_____

2. When might you need a tool to separate a mixture? _____

_____

_____

3. Scientists at Work Scientists often use charts to **record** the results of an investigation. How would setting up charts help you **plan and conduct an investigation**? _____

_____

_____

Investigate Further Make a mixture of sand and water. **Plan and conduct an investigation** to separate the mixture. Would a tool be useful? _____

Which tool would you use? _____

Name _____

Date _____

Plan and Conduct an Investigation

You plan and conduct an investigation to find the answer to a question or to solve a problem.

Think About Planning and Conducting an Investigation

Trey mistakenly dumped a large bag of flour into the kitchen rice container. He planned and conducted two investigations of ways to separate the mixture. He recorded the results of his investigations.

Investigation #1 Made a small mixture of flour and rice in a jar.

Result: Picked the rice out, piece by piece. Took too long. Was not a good method.

Investigation #2 Made a small mixture of flour and rice in a jar. Used a strainer set over a bowl.

Result: Poured mixture into strainer. Flour went through the strainer into bowl. Rice stayed in strainer. Good method for separating the mixture.

1. Why didn't the first investigation work? _____

_____

2. Why did Trey try two investigations before attempting to separate the

large mixture in his kitchen? _____

_____

3. What might have happened if he hadn't done the investigations?

_____

_____

Harcourt

What Are Physical Changes?

Lesson Concept

Physical changes don't form new kinds of matter.

Vocabulary

physical changes (C42)   **mixture** (C43)   **solution** (C44)

Write the letter of the best answer on the lines.

1. In winter the pond water freezes. People skate on the ice. When the

water freezes, _____.

   A new matter is formed   **C** the matter is the same matter

   B the matter becomes a mixture   **D** the matter becomes a solution

2. A young girl cut a sheet of paper into paper dolls. The paper has gone

through a _____.

   A physical change   **B** matter change   **C** state change

3. Emily poured raisins, apple slices, and cinnamon into a bowl. She stirred

them together. The raisins, apple slices, and cinnamon are _____.

   A a solution   **B** a mixture   **C** a condensation

4. A glass of lemonade was left out in the back yard. After a few days, only

the sugar remained. What separated the solution? _____

   A condensation   **B** evaporation   **C** precipitation

5. A solution is a kind of mixture that _____.

   A cannot be eaten   **B** cannot freeze   **C** cannot be separated
                                         by hand

Harcourt

Chemical Changes

Materials

safety goggles

cookie sheet

large glass bowl

measuring cup

baking soda

vinegar

Activity Procedure

1 CAUTION Put on your safety goggles.

2 Place the cookie sheet on the table. Place the bowl on the cookie sheet.

3 **Measure** $\frac{1}{4}$ cup of baking soda. Pour it into the bowl.

4 **Measure** $\frac{1}{4}$ cup of vinegar. Hold the cup with the vinegar in one hand. Use the other hand to fan some of the air from the cup toward your nose. Do not put your nose directly over the cup.

5 Pour the vinegar into the bowl.

6 **Observe** the matter in the bowl. **Record** what it looks like. Use the procedure from Step 4 to smell the matter in the bowl. Record what it smells like.

What it looks like: _____

_____

What it smells like: _____

_____

Harcourt

Name _____

Draw Conclusions

1. How is the material in the bowl like the baking soda and vinegar you

started with? _____

How is it different? _____

2. What can you **infer** about where the bubbles came from?

_____

_____

_____

3. Scientists at Work Scientists do not rely on **conclusions** unless they are
backed by **observations** that can be confirmed. How could you confirm

your observations for this investigation? _____

_____

_____

Investigate Further Mix warm water and a fresh packet of dry yeast.
Observe the mixture. **Record** what you see. What can you **infer** about the

changes you see? _____

_____

_____

Harcourt

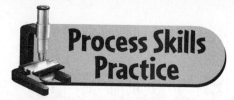

Observe And Infer

You use your senses to observe the world around you. When you infer, you use your observations to form an opinion.

Think About Observing and Inferring

Tasha had some pennies that looked dull and were brown colored. She wanted to find out what the pennies looked like when they were new. She put on safety goggles. She put the pennies in a jar. Then she added 1 cup of vinegar. She noticed the strong smell of the vinegar. She saw that the pennies were not fully covered, so she poured in more vinegar. After 15 minutes she looked in the jar. The pennies were now bright and shiny. They were copper colored just as they were when they were new. The vinegar was dark colored.

1. Why was it important for Tasha to wear safety goggles when she did the experiment? _____

2. What senses did Tasha use in this experiment, and how did she use them?

   _____

   _____

3. What observations did Tasha make about the pennies and the vinegar after the experiment was completed? _____

   _____

4. What can you infer about what changed the color of the pennies?

   _____

   _____

   _____

Harcourt

Name _____

Date _____

What Are Chemical Changes?

Lesson Concept

Chemical changes cause new kinds of matter to form.

Vocabulary

chemical changes (C48)

Use a word from the list below to complete each of the
following statements.

matter	physical	rusting

1. The kind of matter stays the same in _____ changes.

2. _____ is a chemical change that damages metal.

3. In a chemical change, the particles of matter change to form a new kind

of _____.

Answer the questions below.

1. Explain why burning wood is a chemical change.

_____

_____

2. What are some chemical changes that you notice

in your daily life? _____

_____

_____

_____

Harcourt

Recognize Vocabulary

Write the letter of the correct answer in the blank.

1. In a chemical change, two kinds of matter combine to form _____.

   A a different kind of matter   **B** a mixture

2. After a physical change, _____.

   A new matter is formed   **B** matter often looks different

3. A mixture is a substance that contains _____.

   A only one type of matter   **B** two or more types of matter

4. A solution is a mixture of _____.

   A different kinds of particles mixed together evenly   **B** some particles that are mixed together and some that stay apart

Put a check mark on the lines of the paragraphs that talk about chemical changes.

_____ **1.** The Sinclair family is celebrating Jacob Sinclair's fifth birthday with a camping trip. Before they go, Jacob's mother makes cupcakes. She mixes together flour, milk, eggs, butter, and chocolate. She puts the cupcakes in the oven to bake. When they are done, she frosts them.

_____ **2.** Next, Mrs. Sinclair makes a piñata. She cuts up paper and soaks the paper in glue. Then she forms the paper into the shape of a cow. She stuffs the piñata with candy.

_____ **3.** At the campsite that night, the Sinclair family builds a fire in the fire pit. First, the wooden logs go in, and then the fire is lighted. The logs burn brightly, smoke rises in the air, and ashes fall from the burned wood.

_____ **4.** The next morning the family gets ready to go home. They gather up all the trash. They throw the food scraps into a special container and mix them all together. Then they get in the car to drive home.

Chapter 3 • Graphic Organizer for Chapter Concepts

Energy

LESSON 1
WHAT IS ENERGY?

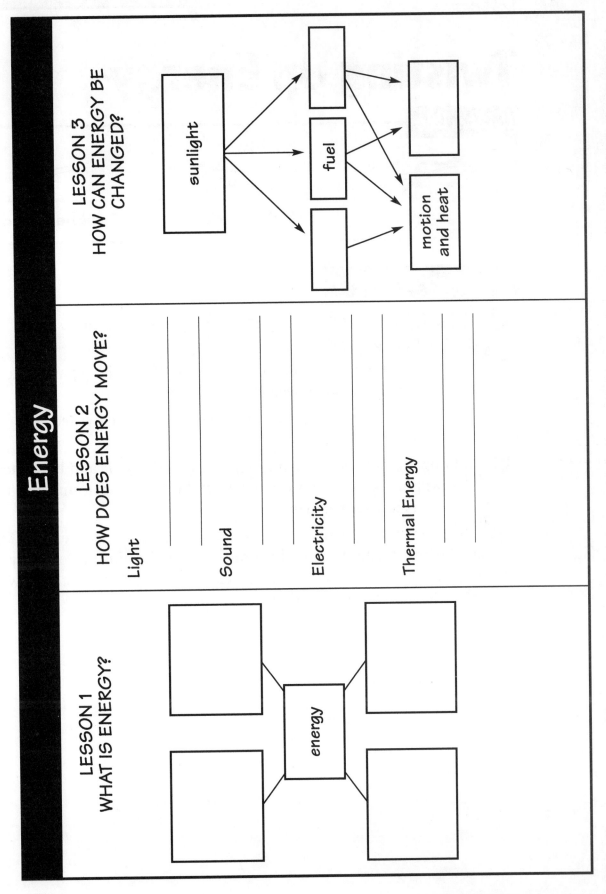

energy

LESSON 2
HOW DOES ENERGY MOVE?

Light _____

Sound _____

Electricity _____

Thermal Energy _____

LESSON 3
HOW CAN ENERGY BE CHANGED?

sunlight

fuel

motion and heat

Name _____

Date _____

Twisting Up Energy

Materials

goggles

2 clothespins

1 rubber band

Activity Procedure

1 **CAUTION** Put on safety goggles to protect your eyes in case a clothespin pops loose.

2 Attach the rubber band to each clothespin. Work with a partner to twist the rubber band between the clothespins.

3 When you have finished, the rubber band should be twisted and curled up.

4 Holding the clothespins tightly, lay them on the table and **hypothesize** what will happen to them when you let them go. **Communicate** your hypothesis to your partner.

5 **Observe** what happens to the clothespins when you let them go. Then do the investigation again, this time twisting the pins more tightly than you did before. **Compare** what the clothespins did the first time with what they did the second time.

Harcourt

Name _____

Draw Conclusions

1. Describe what happened each time you put the clothespins on the table and let go of them. How did your hypothesis compare to the actual

results? _____

_____

_____

2. Where did the energy to move the clothespins come from?

_____

_____

_____

3. **Scientists at Work** Scientists **conduct simple investigations** to learn more about how things work. What did you learn about energy and

twisted rubber bands from your investigation? _____

_____

_____

_____

Investigate Further **Observe** what happens to a third clothespin that you twist around the other two with a second rubber band.

_____

_____

_____

Harcourt

Hypothesize

When you hypothesize before conducting a simple investigation, you are explaining what you think will happen. Your hypothesis can be based on things you have observed, things you already know to be true, or things you have learned from earlier investigations.

Think About Hypothesizing

Harry has a windup toy. He noticed that when he winds it up six twists, it hops twelve times, on average. But when he winds it up three twists, it hops an average of six times. He developed a hypothesis: the toy will always hop twice the number of twists.

1. Where does the windup toy gets its energy? _____

_____

2. How can Harry test his hypothesis? _____

_____

3. How should Harry record his tests? _____

_____

_____

4. What if the results of his tests do not prove his hypothesis? What can he

do? _____

_____

_____

5. If Harry looked inside the toy, what do you think he would find that

stores the energy? _____

_____

Harcourt

Name _____

Date _____

What Is Energy?

Lesson Concept

Energy is the ability to move something. All living things and machines need energy to function. Energy comes mainly from the sun, and can be found in many different forms. It can be stored and used later.

Vocabulary

energy (C62)   **electricity** (C63)   **fossil fuel** (C64)

Draw a line from each living thing or object in the left column to the source of the energy it uses in the right column.

1.

2.

3.

4.

5.

A

B

C

D

E

Use with page C71.

Name _____

Date _____

Waves of Energy

Materials

rope
about 6 feet long

coiled
spring toy

Activity Procedure

1 Do this investigation with a partner. Hold one end of the rope while your partner holds the other. Stand so that the rope hangs loosely between you.

2 While your partner holds his or her end of the rope still, move your end gently up and down. Now move the rope faster. **Compare** what the rope looked like before with what it looks like now.

3 Now take the coiled spring toy and place it on a table or on the floor. Hold one end, and have your partner hold the other.

4 Ask your partner to hold the end still as you quickly push your end in about 4 inches. Now push and pull your end backward and forward. **Observe** what happens to the coils.

5 Draw and label a diagram explaining what happened to the rope when you moved one end. Make another diagram showing what happened to the coiled spring toy when you pushed one end in.

Name _____

Draw Conclusions

1. What happened to the rope when you moved one end up and down? How did it move? What happened when you moved it faster?

_____

_____

_____

_____

2. What happened when you pushed your end of the coiled spring toy toward your partner? What happened when you moved it back and

forth? _____

_____

_____

_____

3. Scientists at Work When things in nature can't be seen, scientists **use models** to see how they work. They then **communicate** what they learn. How did your diagram help you to communicate what you learned about

how energy moves as waves? _____

_____

_____

_____

Harcourt

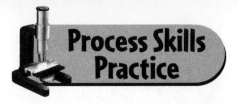

Use Models and Communicate

You can use objects that you can see to model things that you cannot see. Then you can draw and label diagrams to communicate what you have learned. Models can include maps, pictures and diagrams, three-dimensional representations, and computer simulations.

Think About Using Models

We cannot see sounds, but if we observe carefully, we can see and feel the vibrations that make sounds happen. Observe the three pictures below.

1. What would you hear if you plucked the rubber band with your finger?

_____

2. How would the rubber band look while you were hearing the sound?

_____

3. If you placed a vibrating tuning fork into a bowl of water, what would you see?

_____

_____

4. Do sound waves travel through water?

_____

5. If you cover a comb with a piece of wax paper and then hum with your lips touching the wax paper, what would you feel?

_____

Use with page C73.

Harcourt

Concept Review

How Does Energy Move?

Lesson Concept

Energy can move in many different ways. Light energy moves as up-and-down waves. Sound energy moves as back-and-forth waves. Electricity moves from batteries to other objects. Thermal energy moves as heat and is transferred by touching or by radiation.

Vocabulary

vibrate (C77)   **circuit** (C79)

thermal energy (C80)   **water cycle** (C80)

Read the sentence for clues to unscramble the term that belongs in the blank. Then rewrite the unscrambled term in the blank.

1. Sound energy and light move in _____. **VSEAW**

2. Light travels _____ than sound. **STREAF**

3. When you rub your hands together to get them warm, you make

   _____ energy. **MARETLH**

4. In a circuit, energy travels from the _____ through the wires to the bulb. **RABYTET**

5. _____ vibrations can travel through liquids, solids, and gases. **ONDSU**

6. When you feel the thermal energy of hot cocoa in a cup, you are feeling

   _____. **AETH**

7. Thermal energy that moves without touching anything is called

   _____. **AORIDINAT**

8. Fuel is a form of _____ energy. **SEDTOR**

Harcourt

Lighting a Bulb

Materials

masking tape

D-cell battery

2 pieces of insulated electrical wire

miniature light bulb

Activity Procedure

1. Use a piece of masking tape to tape the battery to your desk. This way, it won't roll around.

2. As your partner holds the light bulb a few inches away from the battery, use the wires to connect the ends of the battery with the base of the bulb.

3. Now switch the wires. Do you **observe** any changes?

4. Try to make the bulb light by touching the wires to the glass part of the bulb. Can you make it light?

5. Can you make the bulb light by touching the wires to the sides of the battery?

Harcourt

Name _____

Draw Conclusions

1. What happened when you connected the ends of the battery to the base of the light bulb by using the wires? _____

_____

2. What happened when you switched the wires? _____

_____

3. Could you make the bulb light by touching the wires to the glass part of the bulb? Did the bulb light when you touched the wires to the sides of

the battery? _____

4. Scientists at Work Scientists know that the results of experiments don't often turn out exactly the same every time. This can be caused by differences in materials or differences in procedure. How could you change the materials in this investigation to see if the results would change?

_____

_____

_____

_____

Investigate Further Plan and conduct a simple investigation to find out if you can make the bulb light by using something other than wires to connect the battery and the bulb. **Record** your observations.

_____

_____

_____

_____

Harcourt

Name _____

Date _____

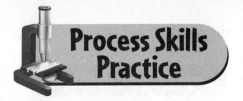

Experiment and Draw Conclusions

When you do an experiment, you make a hypothesis. Then you gather data to test your hypothesis. You can observe and see evidence that helps you draw conclusions about why your hypothesis was—or was not—correct.

Think About Experimenting

In a circuit like the one in Diagram A, the light bulb will light. What do you think will happen if you add another battery to the circuit as in Diagram B?

Diagram A   **Diagram B**

1. Do you think the light bulb will light in the circuit shown in Diagram B?

_____

2. Do you think the light would be brighter in Diagram B? Explain your

answer. _____

_____

3. What do you think would happen if you added two more batteries to the

circuit? _____

_____

Harcourt

How Can Energy Be Changed?

Lesson Concept

Energy can change forms. Sunlight can become food, fuel, or electricity. Electricity can become other kinds of energy, such as light, heat, and motion. Food and fuel can become motion and heat.

Vocabulary

waste heat (C88)

Number these pictures in the correct sequence to show how energy is converted into different forms.

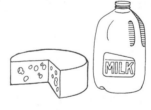

_____

_____

_____

_____

_____

Harcourt

Recognize Vocabulary

In the space provided, write the letter of the term in column B that best fits the definition in column A. Use each term only once.

Column A

_____ 1. The ability to cause change

_____ 2. Where the energy in food comes from

_____ 3. A form of energy that travels through space as up-and-down waves

_____ 4. A form of energy that travels through material as back-and-forth waves

_____ 5. The type of energy found in food and fuel

_____ 6. The kind of energy that powers your refrigerator and your hair dryer

_____ 7. The path electricity follows

_____ 8. The total energy of moving atoms in matter

_____ 9. Thermal energy that moves without touching anything

_____ 10. Fuel formed from organisms that lived millions of years ago

Column B

A electrical

B stored energy

C energy

D radiation

E sound

F fossil fuel

G thermal energy

H light

I circuit

J the sun

Choose two of the vocabulary terms from column B. Then, using your own words, write a sentence that uses each term correctly.

_____

_____

_____

_____

Harcourt

Chapter 4 • Graphic Organizer for Chapter Concepts

Light

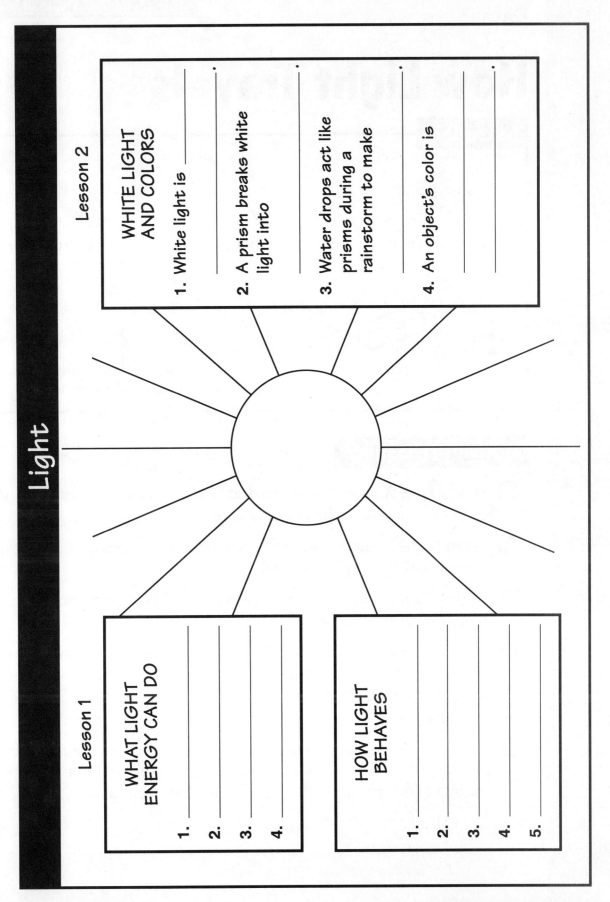

Lesson 2

WHITE LIGHT AND COLORS

1. White light is _____

2. A prism breaks white light into _____

3. Water drops act like prisms during a rainstorm to make _____

4. An object's color is _____

Lesson 1

WHAT LIGHT ENERGY CAN DO

1. _____
2. _____
3. _____
4. _____

HOW LIGHT BEHAVES

1. _____
2. _____
3. _____
4. _____
5. _____

Harcourt

Name _____

Date _____

How Light Travels

Materials

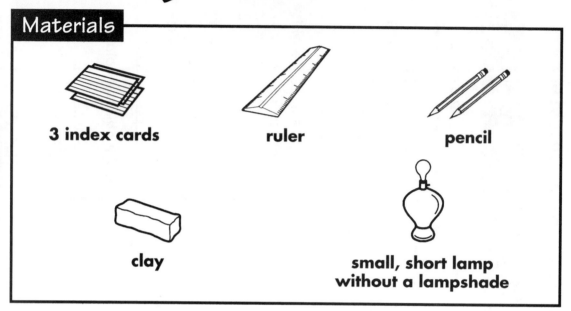

3 index cards   ruler   pencil

clay

small, short lamp
without a lampshade

Activity Procedure

1 Make a large **X** on each card. To draw each line, lay the ruler from one corner of the card to the opposite corner.

2 On each card, make a hole at the place where the lines of the **X** cross. Use the pencil to make the holes.

3 Use the clay to make a stand for each card. Make sure the holes in the cards are the same height.

4 Turn on the light. Look through the holes in the cards. Move the cards around on the table until you can see the light bulb through all three cards at once. Draw a picture showing where the light is and where the cards are.

5 Move the cards around to new places on the table. Each time you move the cards, draw a picture showing where the cards are. Do not move the light! **Observe** the light through the holes each time.

Harcourt

Name _____

Draw Conclusions

1. Where were the cards when you were able to see the light?

_____

_____

_____

2. Were there times you couldn't see the light? Where were the cards then?

_____

_____

_____

3. Scientists at Work Scientists **observe** carefully and then **record** what they observe. Often they draw pictures to **communicate** what they observe. Did drawing pictures help you describe what you saw? Explain.

_____

_____

_____

_____

Harcourt

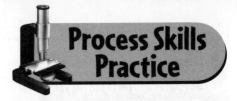

Observe and Communicate

When you observe, you use one or more of your senses to learn about something. You communicate your understanding with others.

Think About Observing and Communicating

Jason spent the weekend at his friend Alex's house. Alex gave Jason a flashlight, so that if Jason had to get up at night, he would be able to see. The first night, Jason decided to go down to the kitchen for a drink of water. He turned on the flashlight and started down the hall. Suddenly he observed what looked like another flashlight shining at him. He realized that his flashlight was shining in a large mirror. He moved closer to the mirror. The flashlight was shining directly at itself. He observed that the light was reflected straight back. When he moved the flashlight around, he observed that the light was no longer reflected straight back in the mirror. In the morning he told Alex about his observations of light. The next night he showed Alex.

1. What was the first observation Jason made about the light from the

flashlight? _____

_____

2. What did Jason do when he realized that the light was coming from

a mirror? _____

3. What was the second observation Jason made? _____

_____

4. How did Jason communicate his observations? _____

_____

_____

Harcourt

How Does Light Behave?

Lesson Concept

Light travels in a straight line unless it bumps into something.
When light hits an object it can be bounced off, bent, or absorbed.

Vocabulary

reflection (C102)   **refraction** (C104)   **absorption** (C106)

Underline the correct answer.

1. You are swimming in a pool. You look down and see that your body
   looks shorter and fatter than it really is. You realize that the light waves
   are bending. What is this called?

   A reflection   **B** refraction   **C** absorption

2. Which of the following is an example of refraction?

   A light moving   **B** an image   **C** an object
      from air to glass   in a mirror   stopping light

Draw your shadow.

3. In the picture on the left, you are standing in your back yard in the
   afternoon. Draw your shadow. Then, in the picture on the right, draw
   your shadow at noon. Put the time of day under your drawings.

Use with page C107.

Making a Rainbow

Materials

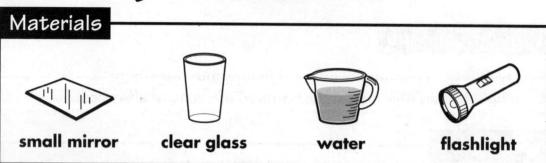

small mirror   clear glass   water   flashlight

Activity Procedure

1 Gently place the mirror into the glass. Slant it up against the side.

2 Fill the glass with water.

3 Set the glass on a table. Turn out the lights. Make the room as dark as possible.

4 Shine the flashlight into the glass of water. Aim for the mirror. Adjust your aim until the light hits the mirror. If necessary, adjust the mirror in the water. Make sure the mirror is slanted.

5 **Observe** what happens to the light in the glass. Look at the light where it hits the ceiling or the wall. **Record** what you observe.

Harcourt

Draw Conclusions

1. What did the light look like as it went into the glass? _____

_____

_____

2. What did the light look like after it came out of the glass? _____

_____

_____

3. Scientists at Work Scientists **draw conclusions** based on what they **observe**. What conclusions can you draw about where color comes from?

_____

_____

Investigate Further Change the angles of the mirror and the flashlight. Which setup gives the best result? Draw a picture of the best arrangement.

_____

_____

_____

Harcourt

Name _____

Date _____

Draw Conclusions

You draw conclusions after you have made observations and gathered data. Conclusions tell what you have learned.

Think About Drawing Conclusions

On a rainy day, Robert put a jar of water on the living room windowsill. He placed a sheet of white paper on the floor. Not very much light came in the window. There was no rainbow on the white paper. Robert drew a conclusion. He wrote it in his notebook. The next day was sunny. Robert did his experiment again. The light passed through the water. A rainbow appeared on the sheet of white paper. Robert wrote down his conclusion about his new experiment.

1. What did Robert observe about his experiment the first time he did it?

_____

_____

2. What was different in Robert's experiment the second time he did it?

_____

3. What do you think Robert's first conclusion might have been?

_____

_____

4. What do you think Robert's second conclusion might have been?

_____

_____

5. What is your conclusion about why a rainbow formed? _____

_____

_____

How Are Light and Color Related?

Lesson Concept

White light is made up of many colors mixed together. A prism can separate the colors.

Vocabulary

prism (C110)

Answer each question with one or more complete sentences.

1. What is a prism? _____

2. Explain how a prism works to separate the colors in white light.

_____

_____

_____

3. A prism breaks white light into its colors. What happens if you add

different-colored lights together? _____

4. Sometimes you can see a rainbow during a summer rain when the sun is

out. How does this happen? _____

_____

5. When white light is separated into colors, the colors always appear in the
same order. Draw a rainbow that shows the colors and their correct order.

_____

_____

Harcourt

Recognize Vocabulary

Fill in each blank with a vocabulary term.

absorption	reflection	prism	refraction

Dear Jenny,

      Yesterday I did an interesting experiment at home. I held a lamp in front of the mirror. I saw that the light from the lamp moved in a straight line to the mirror. After it hit the mirror, it bounced off. I learned that the

word for light bouncing off an object is _____.
Then I went outside to feed the fish in the fish pond. I reached into the water to pick up a piece of paper that didn't belong there. When I looked down, it looked as if my arm was in two pieces! I found out that when light passes from air to water, the light is bent. When light bends, that's called

_____.

      This morning in science class, I learned more about light. When light hits something like a wall, the light is stopped and held in. That's called

_____. Then we really had some fun! My teacher brought something to class so we could make rainbows. When white

light hit the _____, each color of light bent at a different angle. The rainbow was great!

               Your friend,

               Melissa

Answer the question with one or more complete sentences.

The color of an object depends on the reflection and the absorption

of light. How? _____

_____

_____

Harcourt

Chapter 1 • Graphic Organizer for Chapter Concepts

Living Things Depend on One Another

LESSON 1 HOW DO ANIMALS GET FOOD?

They _____

_____ with their environment to get _____ .

_____ interact with sunlight, air, and water to make their own food.

Animals are _____

They eat other living things. _____ eat other living things that have died.

LESSON 2 MODELS OF THESE INTERACTIONS ARE _____ ,

which show how food and energy move from one living thing to another.

which shows how energy decreases at each level of the food chain.

LESSON 3 WHICH IN TURN LEAD TO FOOD WEBS _____ .

A food web is made of _____

Members of the Food Web Are _____ ,

which are animals that hunt and eat other animals.

which are animals that are hunted and used as food.

Harcourt

Name _____

Date _____

Animal Teeth

Materials

blank index cards

books about animals

Activity Procedure

1. **Observe** the pictures of the animals. Look closely at the shape of each animal's teeth.

2. Use one index card for each animal. **Record** the animal's name, and draw the shape of its teeth.

3. With a partner, make a list of words that describe the teeth. **Record** these words next to the drawings on the index cards.

4. Think about the things each animal eats. Use books about animals if you need help. On the back of each index card, make a list of the things the animal eats.

Harcourt

Draw Conclusions

1. Which animals might use their teeth to catch other animals? Which animals might use their teeth to eat plants? Explain.

   _____

   _____

   _____

2. Some animals use their teeth to help them do other things, too. **Observe** the beaver's teeth. How do its teeth help it cut down trees?

   _____

   _____

   _____

3. **Scientists at Work** Scientists learn by **observing**. Scientists can learn about how animals use their teeth by watching how and what the animals eat. From what you observed in this investigation, what can you **infer**

   about the shapes of animals' teeth? _____

   _____

   _____

   _____

Harcourt

Name _____

Date _____

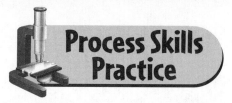

Observe and Infer

When you observe, you use your senses. When you infer, you form an opinion based on what you have observed.

Think About Observing and Inferring

Your class goes on a field trip to a natural history museum. You see a display of wolves in their natural habitat. You observe that these animals have very sharp front teeth. In another display you see pictures of a dairy farm. You learn that cows have flat, grinding teeth. The final display shows the 32 teeth of an adult person. You learn that the front teeth are for cutting food, the teeth next to them are sharp for ripping. The teeth way in the back have a fairly flat surface for grinding food.

1. Think about the cow's teeth. What inference can you make about what

   cows eat? _____

   _____

   _____

2. What inference could you make about the purpose of a person's front

   teeth? _____

3. From your observations of animal teeth, make up an animal. Let it be an animal that eats only plants. Draw a picture showing the teeth of the

   animal. Explain what the animal eats. _____

   _____

   _____

Harcourt

Use with page E5.

Concept Review

How Do Animals Get Food?

Lesson Concept

Plants and animals depend on their environment and on one another to get the food they need.

Vocabulary

interact (E6)   **producer** (E7)

consumer (E7)   **decomposer** (E8)

As you read the summary, fill in each blank with a vocabulary term from above. Answer the questions that follow.

Plants and animals work together, or _____ with the

environment to get what they need. Plants are _____.

They make their own food. Animals are _____. They

must eat plants or other animals. A _____ is a living thing that breaks down once-living things for food.

Make a check mark in front of the statements that agree with your reading.

_____ All living things need food.

_____ All living things have teeth.

_____ Plants interact with sunlight, air, and water to make food.

_____ Animals interact with only living things to get their food.

_____ Consumers can be grouped by the kind of food they eat.

_____ Animals that hunt and kill their food have body parts that help them get their food.

Harcourt

Name _____

Date _____

Make a Food-Chain Model

Materials

index cards

4 pieces of yarn or string

marker

tape

Activity Procedure

1 In the bottom right-hand corners, number the index cards 1 through 5.

2 On Card 1, draw and label grass. On Card 2, draw and label a cricket. On Card 3, draw and label a frog. On Card 4, draw and label a snake. On Card 5, draw and label a hawk.

3 Order the cards in a line with Card 1 first and Card 5 last. Use yarn and tape to connect the cards.

4 Stretch the connected cards out on a table. The cards form a model called a food chain.

5 Discuss with a classmate how each living thing in the food chain gets its food. Tell which things in your model show producers. Tell which things show consumers.

Harcourt

Name _____

Draw Conclusions

1. In your model, which living thing is last in the food chain? Why do you think it is in this place? _____

_____

2. In which part of the food chain is the producer found? Why do you think it is there? _____

_____

_____

3. Scientists at Work Scientists **use models** to help them study things in nature. How does using a model of a food chain help you understand about living things and the food they eat? _____

_____

_____

_____

Harcourt

Name _____

Date _____

Make a Model

Using a model helps you learn about something you cannot observe in real life.

Think About Making a Model

You can make a model of a food chain by using the chart below. Write the names of these animals and plants in the correct columns: a whale; a pelican, which is a bird that eats fish; a small fish; and an ocean plantlike living thing called algae. Fill in the chart as you answer the questions.

Producers	Consumers	Food Chain

Fill in the chart as you answer the questions.

1. What would you list in the *Consumers* column? _____

_____

2. What is a consumer? _____

_____

_____

3. What would you list in the *Producers* column? _____

4. What is a producer? _____

_____

5. In the *Food Chain* column, list the four living things from the paragraph. Write the number *1* next to the living thing or things at the top of the food chain. Number the other living things to show their order in the food chain.

Use with page E11.

Harcourt

Name _____

Date _____

What Are Food Chains?

Lesson Concept

A food chain is the path of food in an ecosystem from one living thing to another.

Vocabulary

food chain (E12)   **energy pyramid** (E14)

Read the summary, and fill in the blanks with vocabulary terms from above.

All living things need energy to live. Living things get their energy from food. Producers get energy from sunlight and store energy in the food they make. Animals cannot make their own food, so they eat other living things.

A _____ shows how energy moves through the

environment. An _____ is a model that shows how the amount of energy in an ecosystem goes down for each animal that is higher in the food chain.

1. Underline the correct answer. A rabbit nibbles on grass. A bird eats a worm. Both animals are ____, which get energy from the food they eat.

consumers   producers   observers   meat-eaters

2. Put this food chain in the correct order by numbering each living thing with a 1, 2, 3, or 4, beginning with the blades of grass.

_____   _____   _____   _____

3. Suppose you have a peanut butter and jelly sandwich for lunch. Do the fillings of your sandwich come from producers or consumers?

_____

Harcourt

Make a Food Web

Materials

index cards, cut into fourths

poster board

tape or glue

crayons

Activity Procedure

1 Write the name of each living thing from the chart on page WB137 on its own card.

2 Glue the cards onto a sheet of poster board so they form a circle. Leave room for writing.

3 Look at the chart again. List two different food chains you could make.

4 Draw arrows between the parts of each food chain. Use a different color for each food chain. You have now made a food web.

5 **Observe** your model to see how the food chains overlap. What other living things could you add to your food web?

Harcourt

Name _____

Living Thing	What It Eats
clover	uses the sun to make its own food
grasshopper	clover
frog	grasshopper
snake	frog, mouse
owl	snake, mouse
mouse	clover

Draw Conclusions

1. What is the producer in this food web? _____

2. What does your food web tell you about producers and consumers?

_____

_____

3. Scientists at Work Scientists sometimes **make models** to help them learn about things. How did drawing a food web help you learn about animals

in a real ecosystem? _____

_____

_____

Investigate Further Cut out magazine pictures of different plants and animals. Work with a partner to make a food web that includes these plants and animals.

Use a Model

When you make a model, you can learn about something that is hard to observe, such as a real-life food web.

Think About Using a Model

Chris visited the wetland near her house. She wrote down some of the things she saw. Some fish splashed in the stream. Caterpillars in the trees munched on new leaves. One fell into the water and was eaten by a fish. A bird swooped down into the water and came out again with a fish in its beak. Grubs crawled on the tree, chewing at the tree's bark. Another bird appeared and picked up one of the grubs in its beak. Chris made drawings of each of the things she saw. She cut out her drawings and glued them to a piece of cardboard. She drew arrows to connect the living things. Now she had a food web. After that, Chris sat down and ate a fish sandwich for lunch. Then she drew a picture of herself and added it to the food web.

1. What is the producer in this food web? _____

2. What are the consumers in this food web? _____

_____

3. List the different food chains in the food web. _____

_____

_____

4. Why did Chris put herself on the food web? _____

_____

5. Make a food web of the different food chains you are a part of.

Harcourt

Name _____

Date _____

What Are Food Webs?

Lesson Concept

A food web is a model that shows how food chains overlap and link together.

Vocabulary

food web (E18) **predator** (E18) **prey** (E18)

Look at the food web. Answer the questions that follow.

1. What is a predator? _____

2. Which of the animals in the food web are predators?

_____

3. What is prey? _____

4. Which of the animals are prey? _____

5. How can an animal, like the frog, be both predator and prey?

_____

_____

Use with page E21.

Recognize Vocabulary

Use the terms below to complete each sentence. The capital
letters will spell a hidden word. Unscramble the capital letters
to spell out the hidden word.

decompoSer	energy pyraMid	foOd chain
food wEb	conSumer	preY
produCer	prEdator	interacT

1. An animal that hunts another animal is called a _____.

2. A model that shows how energy is lost for each higher animal in a food

chain is called an _____.

3. The path of food from one living thing to another is a

_____.

4. An animal that is hunted is called _____.

5. Overlapping food chains are called a _____.

6. A living thing that breaks down the wastes of another living thing is a

_____.

7. When plants and animals work together, they _____.

8. A living thing that eats other living things is a _____.

9. A living thing that makes its own food is a _____.

Hidden Word: All plants and animals interact together to form an

emoyestsc. _____

Chapter 2 • Graphic Organizer for Chapter Concepts

Rocks, Minerals, and Fossils

LESSON 1
MINERALS AND ROCKS

Mineral Properties

1. _____

2. _____

3. _____

Mineral Uses

4. _____

5. _____

6. _____

7. _____

Rocks

8. made of _____

LESSON 2
HOW ROCKS FORM

Three Kinds of Rocks

1. _____

2. _____

3. _____

How Rocks Change
in the Rock Cycle

4. _____

5. _____

6. _____

Uses of Rocks

7. _____

8. _____

9. _____

LESSON 3
FOSSILS

Types of Fossils

1. _____

2. _____

3. _____

4. _____

What Fossils Show

5. _____

Testing Minerals

Materials

Minerals labeled A through G

Activity Procedure

1 Use the chart below.

2 A harder mineral scratches a softer mineral. Try to scratch each of the other minerals with Sample A. **Record** which minerals Sample A scratches.

3 A softer mineral is scratched by a harder mineral. Try to scratch Sample A with each of the other minerals. **Record** which minerals scratch Sample A.

4 Repeat Steps 2 and 3 for each mineral.

5 Using the information in your chart, **order** the minerals from softest to hardest. Give each mineral a number, starting with 1 for the softest mineral.

Mineral to Test	Minerals It Scratches	Minerals that Scratch It
Sample A		
Sample B		
Sample C		
Sample D		
Sample E		
Sample F		
Sample G		

Harcourt

Name _____

Investigate Log

Draw Conclusions

1. Which mineral was the hardest? _____

Which was the softest? _____

How do you know? _____

_____

_____

2. How did you decide the **order** of the minerals? _____

_____

_____

3. **Scientists at Work** Scientists often put objects in **order**. By doing this, they can show that different objects have different properties. How can putting objects in **order** of hardness help you identify them?

_____

_____

Investigate Further To test for hardness, scientists sometimes scratch an unknown mineral with common objects. That's because they don't always have other minerals with them. But to use common objects, scientists need to know how hard the objects are. Using the minerals from this investigation, find out the hardness of glass, a copper penny, and your fingernail. **Record** your observations.

My observations: _____

_____

_____

_____

Observe and Order

Think About Observing and Ordering

Stanley wants to make a display of rocks to bring to class. He goes on a rock-collecting walk. He needs to decide how to order the rocks. He observes the rocks. He sees that the rocks are different colors. There are pink, black, gray, and white rocks. Then he observes that some of the rocks are large and some are medium-sized and some are small. There are also different-shaped rocks in his collection.

1. What are three observations Stanley can make about the rocks?

_____

_____

_____

2. Which sense was used to make those observations? _____

3. How could Stanley order these rocks? _____

_____

4. Draw six different-sized rocks. Label these rocks from **A** to **F**. Put them in order from smallest to largest by writing their letters on the blanks.

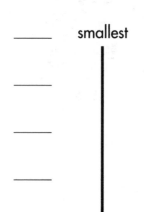

_____ smallest

_____

_____

_____

_____

_____ largest

Harcourt

Name _____

Date _____

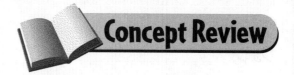

What Are Minerals and Rocks?

Lesson Concept

A mineral is a solid natural material that has never been alive.
Rocks are made of minerals.

Vocabulary

mineral (E32) **rock** (E34) **core** (E34) **mantle** (E34) **crust** (E34)

Match each term with its definition on the right.

1. rock   **A** hot middle layer of Earth

2. crust   **B** a solid substance made of minerals

3. mantle   **C** the center of Earth

4. core   **D** the solid outside layer of Earth

5. mineral   **E** a solid natural object that has never been alive

This drawing shows Earth cut open. Label each layer with a term from the vocabulary box.

6. _____

7. _____

8. _____

Use with page E37.

Name _____

Date _____

Types of Rocks

Materials

3 rocks labeled I, S, and M

3 rocks labeled 1, 2, and 3

hand lens

Activity Procedure

1 Use the chart below.

2 Rocks *I*, *S*, and *M* are three different types of rocks. Look at them with and without the hand lens. **Record** your observations in the chart.

3 Look at each of the numbered rocks with and without the hand lens. **Record** your observations in the chart.

4 **Compare** the properties of the lettered rocks with the properties of the numbered rocks. Think about how the rocks are alike and how they are different.

Rock	Observations
I	
S	
M	
1	
2	
3	

Harcourt

Name _____

Draw Conclusions

1. What properties did you use to **compare** the rocks?

_____

_____

_____

2. Which numbered rock is most like Rock I? _____

Explain your answer. _____

_____

Which numbered rock is most like Rock S? _____

Explain your answer. _____

_____

Which numbered rock is most like Rock M? _____

Explain your answer. _____

_____

3. Scientists at Work Scientists learn about new objects when they **compare** them with objects they have already studied. What did you learn about the rocks when you compared them?

_____

_____

Investigate Further Look near your school or home for small rocks. **Compare** them with Rocks *I*, *S* and *M*. Try to **classify** the rocks as *I*, *S*, or *M*.

_____

_____

Harcourt

Compare and Observe

Think About Comparing and Observing

Diego's class went to a natural history museum to see an exhibition of rocks. The next day his teacher gave the students a worksheet to fill out.

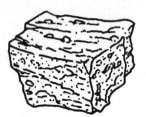  

Rock 1   **Rock 2**   **Rock 3**   **Rock 4**

1. Look at the four rocks above. Name three properties of the rocks you

   can observe. _____

2. Which of the two rocks are similar? Rock _____ and Rock _____

3. Compare the two rocks. Which two properties are the same?

   _____

4. Compare Rock 1 and Rock 2. In what ways are they different from each other?

   _____

   _____

   _____

5. Why is it important to make good observations before you compare?

   _____

   _____

   _____

Harcourt

Concept Review

How Do Rocks Form?

Lesson Concept

There are three types of rocks—igneous, sedimentary, and metamorphic.

Vocabulary

sedimentary rock (E38)   **igneous rock** (E38)

metamorphic rock (E38)   **rock cycle** (E40)

Write the letter of the best answer on the lines.

1. Rocks are grouped by how they _____.

   A melt   **B** change   **C** form

2. Rocks can be changed by heat and pressure, melting, and the effects of

   _____.

   A wind and water   **B** cloud formations   **C** farming

3. After the material from an exploding volcano cools and hardens, _____ rocks can form.

   A metamorphic   **B** igneous   **C** sedimentary

4. Write about some of the ways you use rocks in the classroom.

_____

_____

5. Draw a sedimentary rock.

Harcourt

Name _____

Date _____

Fossil Layers

Materials

5 colors of modeling clay

5 different seashells labeled A through E

5 sheets of wax paper

Activity Procedure

1 Use the chart below.

2 Use clay of one color to make a layer about the size and shape of a hamburger. Put the layer of clay on a sheet of wax paper.

3 Press a shell into the clay to make a print. Remove the shell. **Record** the clay color and the shell letter in your chart.

4 Place a sheet of wax paper over the clay layer.

5 Repeat Steps 2, 3, and 4 until you have made new layers with each color of clay and each shell.

Rock Layer	Clay Color	Shell Letter
1 (bottom layer)		
2		
3		
4		
5 (top layer)		

Harcourt

Name _____

6 Trade your group's clay layers and
shells with another group's. Make a second chart. Remove each layer of
clay, and **observe** it. Do not change the order of the layers. Match each
shell to its print. Fill in the second chart. Check your answers with the
group that made the model.

Draw Conclusions

1. How did you know the correct layer for each shell?

_____

2. Pretend the shell prints are fossils and the clay is sedimentary rock. List
the shell letters from the oldest to the newest. Do this by using what you

know about sedimentary rock layers. _____

_____

_____

3. **Scientists at Work** Scientists **use models** to understand how things
happen. How did **using a model** help you understand how fossils are left

in layers in time order? _____

_____

_____

_____

Harcourt

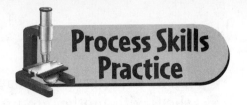

Use a Model

Think About Using a Model

Shawna decided to make a model of a shell mold to help her understand how fossils are preserved. She mixed up some wet mud and half-filled a plastic margarine tub. She pressed a shell into the mud and covered it with more mud. She let the mud mixture dry in the sun for four days. Then she broke apart the mold, being careful not to disturb the mud below the shell.

1. Why might you use a model to find out about how fossils are preserved?

_____

_____

_____

2. What problems do you think there would be in recovering fossil prints from hardened mud?

_____

_____

3. What do you think Shawna saw after she broke open her mold?

_____

_____

4. Draw what you think Shawna saw.

Harcourt

What Are Fossils?

Lesson Concept

A fossil is something that has lasted from a living thing that died long ago.

Vocabulary

fossil (E46)

Put a check mark in front of the true statement in each pair.

_____ **1.** Sedimentary rocks usually have more fossils than other rocks because heat and pressure help preserve the fossil.

_____ Sedimentary rocks usually have more fossils than other rocks because what's left of a plant or animal is trapped in the sediments that form the layers of the rock.

_____ **2.** Fossils can show the color of an animal that lived long ago.

_____ Fossils can show the shape of an animal that lived long ago.

_____ **3.** A mold is the shape of a plant or animal left in sediments when the rock formed.

_____ A mold is the imprint of a leaf or another thin object.

_____ **4.** A cast has the exact shape of the animal that made the mold.

_____ A cast always has a small piece of bone in the mold.

5. Explain how this mold formed.

_____

_____

_____

_____

_____

Harcourt

Recognize Vocabulary

Fill in the blanks with the correct term from the box. Then find
the words and circle them in the word search puzzle.

mineral	rock	crust	mantle
core	rock cycle	fossil	

1. A solid object that was formed in nature and has never been alive is likely

to be a _____.

2. The surface layer of Earth is called the _____.

3. The _____ is the
middle layer of Earth.

4. At the center of Earth is the hottest layer,

called the _____.

5. A _____ is made
of minerals.

6. A _____ is a thing
that has lasted from a living thing that
died long ago.

O	F	M	A	N	C	M
R	O	C	K	U	R	A
F	S	T	U	R	A	N
S	S	C	R	U	S	T
M	I	N	E	R	A	L
T	L	T	A	U	L	E
L	E	C	O	R	E	N

Read the sentences. Write the correct letter of the term on the lines.

A metamorphic rock	**B** sedimentary rock	**C** igneous rock

_____ **7.** It is a type of melted rock that has cooled and hardened.

_____ **8.** This rock forms from material that settles into layers.

_____ **9.** Heat and pressure have changed other rocks into this type of rock.

Harcourt